The Incredible Duchess

DORIS LESLIE

The
Incredible Duchess

The Life and Times of
Elizabeth Chudleigh

HEINEMANN: LONDON

William Heinemann Ltd
15 Queen Street, Mayfair, London W1X 8BE

LONDON   MELBOURNE   TORONTO
JOHANNESBURG   AUCKLAND

First published 1974
© Doris Leslie 1974

434 41825 0

S15526
F.

Printed in Great Britain by Cox & Wyman Ltd
London, Fakenham and Reading

FOREWORD

In presenting this life of Elizabeth Chudleigh, the most famous, or infamous, woman of her time, I have adhered strictly to fact. No character or name of character or excerpt from letters quoted is fictitious. Wherever possible I have reproduced the actual dialogue as recorded by her contemporaries in their numerous memoirs and journals, in particular from the letters of Horace Walpole.

Elizabeth Chudleigh was known as the Duchess of Kingston and her two marriages, legal or illegal, produced the *cause célèbre* of the eighteenth century. Yet, despite all that has been written or handed down to us about her, she will remain for ever an enigma.

A brief bibliography of authorities consulted will be found at the end of the book.

DORIS LESLIE

PROLOGUE

'Guilty upon mine honour!'

She who had fled from the London that had reviled her, had rejoiced in her disgrace; she who had been loved by men of the highest in the land, whispered these words echoed in the thoughts that whirled about her where she sat in the bows of the fishing boat which ploughed its way through the trough of the waves. . . . Yes, a fishing boat, squalid and stinking of its catch. She had ordered the captain of her own yacht to commandeer this disgusting trawler to take her from Dover to Calais rather than face the stares and hear the muttered remarks of her English crew, who knew, and who did not know, of that nine days' wonder when all England had gloatingly followed her trial attended by the King, the Queen, the Court, and the hoi polloi of London. This, then, the end of it. What now?

'Publicly unduchessed' (as that sprightliest of gossips, Mrs Delaney, delighted to put it), she had made no definite plans for her future more than to seek the hospitable welcome of France at the hotel in Calais where she had formerly been received with obsequious ceremony. That was when she had left Thoresby, one of her husband's ducal seats, had left him to a little milliner in a moment of pique, 'to raise himself a feeble horn'. She was not squeamish in her choice of inelegant vernacular in vogue among the blades of St James's as much as in the stews of St Giles, to damn him with too intimate an interest in a young person thirty years his junior. . . . So, in her first flush of indignation, she had left him and was back within three months, contrite, and no more was said or heard of the 'young person'.

Now he was dead and she neither his wife nor his widow and: 'Guilty, erroneously but not intentionally, upon mine honour', as voiced by the only one of her peers who, hand on heart, had spoken in her vindication. Well, so it was, and here am I, 'unduchessed'. . . . A mirthless laugh escaped her as she pulled her soaking cloak about her shoulders and called above the howl of the wind in the sails for her maids. No answer from the huddled group of seasick women lying prostrate on the slimy deck; none but her little black page, pale green beneath his ebony skin.

'Grace, you call, you wish . . .?'

'A cup of broth to warm me. I perish. You, too, poor child.'

But it was not the warm welcome she had expected from Dessein, the landlord of the inn at Calais, who already had news of her downfall and believed her lost of her fortune along with her strawberry leaves. . . . A small room at the top of the house was offered her, furnished with a bed and not much else. There her dauntless spirit flagged, and she too weary to argue or upbraid him, allowed herself to be undressed by one of her women the least affected from the lamentable crossing. Loud in protest at her lady's plight she vowed to have that despicable man's ears shaved from his head, and was bidden:

'Leave me. He will be dealt with when I've slept. You to your room with the rest of them.'

And sleep she did for eight hours and woke to a shaft of sunlight piercing the shutters. With a knock at the door came Dessein in answer to her summons to enter, if not on his knees, nose bowed to them.

Further news retailed by the captain of her yacht who skippered the trawler, and had heard of the contents so far unpacked from her numerous baggage, entirely

2

reversed his opinion of the lady's loss not only of title but of wealth. If not Madame la Duchesse she was still Madame la Comtesse, and the legal inheritor of the late Duke's entire estate.

Volubly apologetic, he explained that he had been unprepared for the arrival of Madame la Duchesse, tact-fully according her the nobility from which she had been deprived, but that the suite with which he had been honoured for Madame la Duchesse to occupy on her previous visit had not been available the night before. *Enfin!* He had dismissed those others (accompanied by Gallic disparaging shrugs) whom he had turned away to prepare the rooms in readiness for Madame la . . .

She cut him short.

'Assez!' her French was execrable but sufficed to tell him, 'J'ong ay assez de vot' blague. Envoyez moy mes femmes de chambers et ma dayjeunay. Caffee O lait ay les crossons.'

'Oui, Madame, tout de suite.'

He bowed himself out and her women came in, attended to her toilet, and conducted her to the suite now in readiness to receive her.

She breakfasted on delicious croissants, honey and coffee 'which only the French know how to make', she told a maid, busy with her coiffure. Then, couched on pillows covered in finest silk unpacked from her trunks, she allowed herself the luxury of reminiscence, her thoughts searching back along the years when she . . . How near the present is to the past as we tread the down-ward path to our older age, she reflected. But I am not yet old. I will never be old . . . *'I am years older, though younger, than you, you peaky-faced knock-kneed mother's boy. Who's your father?'*

'My father is Prime Minister of England!'

3

ONE

'. . . Prime Minister of England!'

'Go tell that to the Marines. There's one – that old pensioner yonder. He's a soldier sailor 'cause he fought in sea battles against the Dutch when King Charles was King . . . Mother's boy!'

She flung at his head the core of the apple she was munching, perched in the trunk of a tree in the garden of her father's house at Chelsea. He was Governor of the Hospital for veteran war pensioners, and she and the boy next door would often play in the gardens of the hospital where her father's grounds encroached upon those of Sir Robert Walpole.

'I tell you my father *is* Prime Minister of England!'

'Who said he isn't, but he's not your father.'

The boy whom she joyed to tease fisted his hands and, dodging the apple core, rushed to drag her from her perch shouting in his squeaky treble:

'You'll say that once too often, and if you weren't a girl, I'd call you out.'

'Call me out where?'

'Where insults are revenged by gentlemen of honour.'

'Go on then. Call me out. I may not be a gentleman of honour – which you aren't – but I'm a lady.'

'You are not. You're just a vain conceited spoilt little adjectival –'

'What long words you use. How do you learn them?'

'From my books. The seats of learning.'

'Talk of vain, conceited – you're the vainest, conceitedest, stupidest –'

'Children!' Mrs Chudleigh, wife of the Governor

5

Colonel, advanced upon the pair of them. 'Sir Robert is here and asks for you, Elizabeth. You too, Horace, come to your father. Lady Mary is also here and – Gracious goodness, child! Your hands, your hair, your face! Go wash yourself. Horace, you are always neat and tidy. Elizabeth, go in before me. Horace –' she gestured him to follow her. Bowing low – he lacked nothing of good grace if of good looks – he obeyed. Elizabeth poked her tongue at him mouthing the words: 'Neat and tidy, spick and spanny, little manny, mother's boy!'

She would always get the best of it when sparring with Horace even should they come to blows if he, goaded by her jeers, might be given to retaliate with a smarting cuff returned with tooth and claw. Yet on the whole the two were fond enough playmates, and she always ready to take his part when his father's other sons and the sons of the Dukes of Ancaster and Hamilton, whose estates facing the river marched with Sir Robert's and were playgrounds for the children, made fun of the delicate little spindle-legged boy with the long, pale, elderly face.

The gossip of ladies of the Court, forgathered in those great houses on the Thames, was not lost upon their young: that the Prime Minister, a complaisant enough husband, shut eyes and ears to tales that gave this third of his sons the parentage of Carr, Lord Hervey. Sir Robert had sufficient illicit entanglements to deal with in his own home to probe too deeply into his wife's extra-marital amusements.

Elizabeth, whose hands but not her face had undergone attention, was a favourite of the Prime Minister. Burly, rubicund, double-chinned and prematurely white, Sir Robert bestowed a kiss on her grubby cheek and remarked upon her eyelashes: 'So long you could hang rings on 'em!'

'Mine were longer than hers till the smallpox lost me of them all,' said Lady Mary Wortley Montagu, once the

6

Toast of London* and wife of the late Ambassador to Constantinople. When her husband returned to England, ignominiously relieved of his Ministry at the Porte, Lady Mary had been disfavoured by the First George, then King, and his two ugly German mistresses.

The cause for her fall from grace with the leery, beery successor to Queen Anne, last of the Stuarts, was that Lady Mary had brought with her a case full of walnut shells. 'Nothing suspiciously harmful in that,' was the opinion of those who had not known that these seemingly innocuous walnut shells contained, as discovered by her ladyship in the Sultan's harem, the pus of the prevalent scourge of smallpox virtually non-existent in Turkey, and of which in England Lady Mary had been a victim, as had her much loved brother who died of it.

But the loss of Lady Mary's eyelashes may have troubled her more than the lack of recognition for the discovery contained in those 'damnable walnut shells'.

' 'Tis a pretty child and would be a beauty were she washed,' dispassionately remarked her ladyship, raising a quizzing glass to her lashless eyes that still held much of the brilliance that had enslaved a dwarfish hunchbacked poet, not then one of the immortals, who, in revenge for her ridicule of him, likened her in blistering lines to 'a furious Sappho, poxed by her love and libelled by her hate!'

Yet Pope had still to do his worst to Lady Mary when the child, destined to wed the lady's nephew, the Duke of Kingston, sat to be fondled by the father of the boy destined in his turn to immortality as the writer of those incomparable letters in which so much gall is mingled with the ink.

But the very young Elizabeth Chudleigh, accustomed to admiration of her beauty whether washed or unwashed, paid less heed to Lady Mary's scrutiny than to Horace standing sulky mouthed and unnoticed in a corner while

*See *A Toast to Lady Mary.*

his precociously malicious mind registered the talk that now veered toward the latest topic of the day.

The King's callous indifference to the death of his wife, Sophia Dorothea, whom for more than thirty years he had kept imprisoned in a gaunt barrack of a house at Ahlden for her alleged adultery with the handsome unscrupulous Swede Count Königsmarck,* had aroused not only the indignation of the Court but that of His Majesty's lesser subjects; for on the day of the announcement of his wife's death he appeared at the playhouse accompanied by his two mistresses. One of these, the Duchess of Kendal, nicknamed 'the Maypole' for her tall and unpleasantly attenuated figure, was originally Frau Schulemberg, and had been raised to the peerage together with her rival favourite, Frau Kielmansegge, now Countess of Darlington, as hideously fat as the 'Maypole' was thin, and known by the Court and a grinning public as 'The Elephant'.

'Considering how the King flaunted his odious women for all of us to see,' said Mrs Chudleigh, 'he might have had the decency to preserve some restraint or pretence of mourning for the poor princess whom he so shamefully wronged.'

'The Maypole,' remarked Lady Mary, never at a loss to condemn where condemnation was deserved, 'has rooked our German George of seven thousand five hundred a year as compensation for her having speculated too unwisely, as did too many of us, in the South Sea Bubble which burst, to ruin half the population.'

A somewhat tactless reminder, since the Governor General of the hospital, Colonel Chudleigh, had speculated in the fraudulent South Sea Company of some few years before to lose him almost his entire capital. Lady Mary had also, she said, had her 'little flutter', but as her husband was a millionaire she could afford to lose. Not so Colonel Chudleigh. He still held by grace and favour his rent-free

*See *The Rebel Princess*.

8

house at Chelsea adjacent to the hospital, but could not now sustain the upkeep of his house in Devonshire where Elizabeth presumably was born; however, he does not appear to have sold the Devon property, which would revert to his daughter at her parents' death.

This talk between her elders conveyed nothing to Elizabeth save for the one word 'Bubble' on which she pounced. Freeing herself from Sir Robert's encircling arm, she scrambled down from his knee and ran to the scowling Horace.

'We blow bubbles, Horace and me – don't we, Horace?'

'Not "me". And *I*,' said he glaring at her. 'Try to speak the King's English even if he can't.'

'And me then – and I – me – we *do* blow bubbles,' she turned to the amused Lady Mary who, overhearing Horace's correction, told Sir Robert:

'That son of yours should go far to follow in your steps, maybe.'

'He had better not,' replied the Prime Minister. 'To carry the burden of a nation on his too-slender shoulders would break him as it looks to break me.'

'But we *do* blow bubbles,' doggedly pursued Elizabeth. 'One of the old pensioners gave me a pipe – a long clay thing and when *I* blow them they go floating over the trees but Horace's bubbles go burst before they get there. I always win!'

Yes, she would always win . . . until the last.

The catastrophic South Sea Bubble that had plunged thousands to the verge of suicide in their delirium for gambling and had so seriously involved the Governor of Chelsea Hospital, may have been a factor in his too early death which succeeded that of England's King by a few weeks.

'The King is dead!' joyfully proclaimed his subjects. 'Long live the King!' There were many who hoped that he would not, despite that he could speak English, if in a strong Teutonic guttural, and was better liked than his father had been or by the loyalists who clung to the memory of their loved Stuarts.

When he was duly crowned at Westminster Hall the widowed Mrs Chudleigh with her little daughter had the privilege, accorded her doubtless by reason of her friendship with the Prime Minister, of witnessing the ceremony. To the child seated among that vast audience, dazzled by the splendid robes of peers and peeresses, and more than all by the magnificent presence of Queen Caroline, Consort of the stout, strutting, pigeon-chested Monarch, bowing and grinning right and left from under his golden canopy, she could not have foreseen that at some distant future she would be no spectator but the central figure of a scene to be enacted in that same Hall, and which would become the *cause célèbre* of the whole century. . . . She saw nothing but the glorious sight of the Queen. Her garments, caught in the mingled light of candles and sun, prismatically drawing rainbow sparks from the myriad diamonds and other jewels that bestrewed her robes were valued, it was said, at a quarter of a million.

But the enthusiasm of the seven-year-old Elizabeth was not echoed by that cynical and witty observer, Lady Mary Wortley Montagu, who found the whole performance, no less than the performers, ridiculous.

'Some languished, others strutted.' One, the Duchess of Montrose, was described as 'creeping along with a dozen black snakes playing round her face'. Another, Lady Portland, is represented as 'an Egyptian mummy, embroidered over with hieroglyphics. . . .'

Lady Mary's record of the society and times in which she lived has filled volumes and can only be comparable, but with less stylistic elegance if in equal wit, to those of Horace Walpole, too young at the time of this Second George's Coronation to have given us his views on it.

Suffice that the King is crowned, and that his son, Prince Frederick and his son's wife, Augusta, were set up in a separate establishment at Leicester Fields, each to play their part in this astonishing tragi-comedy, the life of Elizabeth Chudleigh.

*　　　*　　　*

Mrs Chudleigh was a woman of resource and of that same indomitable courage which her daughter inherited from her, and little else. Since her bereavement which deprived her of the Governor's house at Chelsea, his widow was left to face a penurious existence and, as best she might, struggle to recover a substitute for the rank and position she had lost.

It did not suit her purpose to leave London and her late husband's influential connections, although she still retained the small property in Devonshire where, if all else failed, she could retire with Elizabeth. Yet that must be one last resource. She well realized that by isolating her daughter in the wilds of the country she might lose her the chance of making an eligible match. With the promise of beauty already in its bud she could secure for Elizabeth a future after her ambitious mother's heart if she remained in London. Mrs Chudleigh therefore rented a house that though not in the most fashionable district was sufficiently select on the outskirts of the village of Chelsea and within walking distance of the estates of the Dukes of Hamilton and Ancaster, whose sons were Elizabeth's playmates.

In order to keep up appearances Mrs Chudleigh 'accommodated', as she put it, 'an inmate' of her house, or in words less carefully chosen, a lodger.

In an age when girls were married at fifteen Elizabeth had yet a few years before she could be entered for the marriage market. In the meantime her mother cared for her education which in those days was considered enough if begun at eight years old and ended at fifteen. In this eighteenth century all that was considered necessary for the accomplishments of the daughter of a gentleman was that she could read tolerably well, write legibly a little more than her own name, without too erroneous misuse of syntax, the use of the globes, poise and deportment, and a smattering of French. These elementary rudiments of knowledge were imbibed by Elizabeth under her mother's doubtful tuition until she was sixteen.

For ten years Mrs Chudleigh, after her husband's death, endeavoured to make ends meet and still retain her position in the circle of Leicester House where Frederick Prince of Wales and his long-suffering wife held their Court which was even more disreputable than that of his father whose death would bring Frederick's son to the Throne and to St James's.

This would considerably change Mrs Chudleigh's position in the social sphere where she was accustomed to be received and to enjoy the friendship not only of the Prime Minister but of Royalty, for the then Princess Caroline had, upon occasion, graciously favoured with a visit the widow of the Governor of Chelsea Hospital, of which the Princess had been a patron. But now as Consort of the reigning monarch such visits were terminated, as were also those of Sir Robert Walpole and the interchange of gossip over dishes of tea.

Walpole had all to do to hold his ministerial ascendancy against the strong opposition of Pulteney, the leader of the Whigs, afterwards created Earl of Bath. This second George had loathed his father, chiefly for the merciless treatment his mother had suffered as a prisoner at Ahlden, forbidden sight of or any communication with her children. Her son George as a boy did make one attempt to scale the walls of the gloomy stronghold that guarded his mother but was hauled back by the then Elector of Hanover's servants. Consequently when he became King, the ministers of state under the late monarch were anathema to the son who was determined to be rid of the lot of them. Pulteney had been high in the running for the premiership, in fact both he and Walpole bid against each other for the King's first choice. Pulteney offered himself with £800,000, but Walpole outbid him by another hundred thousand, and so: 'Our Georgie has been put up for auction', cackled the blades of St James's.

Mrs Chudleigh now realized that her girl's hope of a splendid match had dwindled to the barest chance, since she had no entry to the Court where the former Prince and Princess of Wales had held sway. As an impoverished widow who took in a lodger, or lodgers, no matter how 'accommodated' were her 'inmates', she could hardly hope to be received at His Majesty's Court. While undecided whether she should or should not leave London for the Devonshire house where she might hope to secure if not a title for Elizabeth at least a wealthy squire, fate decided for her. Elizabeth was taken with the smallpox, a mild case that left her unscarred and which the doctors in those days of unenlightened medical knowledge often confused with chicken pox, which it most probably was since not a mark had been left on the perfect skin of her face. But she was none the less debilitated and Mrs Chudleigh's doctor advised her to 'get her away'. There was cholera on Thameside down at Chelsea.

To Devonshire therefore was Elizabeth reluctantly removed not only from fear of infection from cholera but from the possible gaieties and glamour of London's social life of dining and dancing in the garden of Vauxhall, where, although still barely sixteen, she had already tasted the sweets thereof, having entertained her first amatory friendship with a boy a year older than herself.

So we have it that Elizabeth, riding along a country lane – she always rode unattended, against her mother's command, which she seldom if ever obeyed – dismounted to pick blackberries from the tall hedges that lined the way. The honey-gold September sun lighted her warm brown hair to a burnished bronze. She was of that age between the bud and blossom that had already captivated the sons of the bucolic hunting squires, her mother's neighbours for whom Elizabeth had no use; she disdained their amorous advances. Even in her late teens her day-dreams envisaged herself as the wife of some great nobleman, instilled by her mother's persistent ambition, not, however, to be realized in a Devonshire village.

Pulteney, on his doctor's advice, as Mrs Chudleigh had been advised for her daughter's health, had also come to the country to recover from an illness far from the onerous problems of statesmanship and for a temporary respite, as was said, from 'the misfortune of being damned in a fair wife', cursed with an abominable temper but of extraordinary beauty if of low birth.

He, too, riding on that September morning, came from a wood that bordered the lane and, sighting Elizabeth, looked and looked again, halted his horse, and baring his head, bowed from the saddle, and:

'Madam,' said he, 'it is seldom one is so fortunate as to come out of a wood and meet a divinity.'

We have only her word for it, but it is not unlikely he could turn a pretty phrase to compliment a pretty woman.

And that is how Pulteney, leader of the Opposition Whigs, claimed as he said to have 'discovered' Elizabeth Chudleigh who he thought was a 'simple country girl'.

He proved to be mistaken.

There was nothing 'simple' about Elizabeth other than a childish readiness in response to affection. Her natural wit, vivacity and provocative beauty which seems to have been an emanation of beauty rather than the physical loveliness attributed to her, charmed this elderly admirer as it would charm men of higher rank.

Even at that early age, Elizabeth could not have been unaware of the advantage to be gained by the interest of so politically important and influential a gentleman as Mr Pulteney. But his interest in her was no more than a pleasurable relaxation in that rural retreat, to 'cultivate', as he recorded, 'so receptive a young mind'. Pulteney, nothing if not a prude, would have avoided any romantic implication in their relationship. His disillusioned marriage had rendered him something of a misogynist.

To undertake the neglected education of this unsophisticated country girl may have proved a disappointment, in that his instruction and the books he gave her to read and his endeavours to cultivate her 'receptive young mind', produced barely concealed yawns and, as he put it, 'pretty pouts'.

She did however bear with him and his boring tuition for she had learned, if not Latin which he essayed to teach her, but of his intimacy with Prince Frederick and Princess Augusta, Prince and Princess of Wales, on the accession of Prince Frederick's father, George, the Second.

Although Mrs Chudleigh had lost, when she lost her husband, the visits of royalty to the Governor's house at Chelsea, there was still the Princess of Wales as a possible patroness, and Elizabeth required no urging from her mother to make herself agreeable to Mr Pulteney whose attentions if not 'romantic' were something more than entirely platonic.

Possibly because Elizabeth had been taken under the elderly wing of Mr Pulteney and had gained a reputation in Devonshire as a girl of infinite attraction, a rising young artist, a Mr Joshua Reynolds, sought her acquaintance, was struck with her beauty and asked her to sit to him for her portrait. It is unlikely that Pulteney commissioned Reynolds to paint her for he was notoriously parsimonious, and one of his contemporaries has said of him: 'He studied the value of a penny to a nicety and would declare that with the price of a pot of porter in his pocket he would buy only a pint.' This may have been malice for Pulteney was greatly disliked by the members of the rival party headed by Prime Minister Walpole; but there is no evidence that he gave Elizabeth gifts, trinkets and such-like other than the seeds of learning from which she gained nothing of material worth.

Yet what she did gain, after much pleading and more 'pretty pouts', was the promise, prompted by her mother and wheedled out of Pulteney, that he would suggest her to the Princess Augusta of Wales as a Maid of Honour. . . . The ambition of a mother would now be realized beyond her dreams.

Elizabeth Chudleigh was accepted and became Maid of Honour to the Princess of Wales!

*   *   *

Great was the rejoicing of Mrs Chudleigh when Elizabeth came to Leicester House. The Maids of Honour, euphemistically styled, in waiting on the Princess of Wales were in more intimate degree in waiting on the Prince.

These young ladies, for the most part well known both in and out of Court for the various scandals attached to their names, enchanted the gossips – and the Prince of Wales. Leicester House was in even greater disrepute than the Court of the King at St James's. Why Frederick's mother, Queen Caroline, the most accomplished and loveliest of German princesses, should have chosen to take as husband the pop-eyed, staring, red-faced princeling of the Britain to which his father had succeeded indirectly from the Royal Stuarts, and remained a faithful and devoted wife until her death, is incomprehensible.

George the Second had little to recommend him save that he spoke sufficient English – although he and his wife almost always spoke together in French – other than that he was a dapper little man, careful of his dress, gallant in love and war, especially in war. He had been proved a courageous soldier under Marlborough and distinguished himself in particular at Oudenarde. It is not legendary but historically authentic that, blubbering at the bedside of his wife when she lay dying and attempting to soothe him by begging him to marry again, he answered her:

'Non, non! Jamais! J'aurai des maîtresses'.... As if he had not already had a dozen. Nor did he marry again because, after his fashion, he loved her and mourned her with genuine grief all the rest of his life.

But there was no love lost between this King George and his son, heir to the throne he would never ascend. We have it that Frederick detested his father even more than his father detested him, although there was no reason why this King George should hate his son as he had hated his father George the First for his monstrous cruelty to and imprisonment of his wife who should have been Queen Consort, and whom George could only remember as the mother he, as a child, had adored and was later forbidden to see.

When Elizabeth came to Leicester House she found, if gossip could be credited, she must have been the only Maid of Honour who was still a 'maid'.

Always ready to seize upon advantageous opportunity, Elizabeth, unlike her sister Maids, served her mistress with deference, loyalty and genuine devotion. Naturally warm-hearted, she realized that the Princess, for all her high position as future Queen of England, was just a lonely, neglected little German girl, and that the rest of her Maids scarcely gave her the homage and attention which was her due. The only homage and attention they gave was to the Prince in the hope of being the one chosen for his fancy. Quite a few of them were, but not Elizabeth. From the moment she came to Court he had his ogling eye on her, and more than once had made unmistakable overtures to Mrs Chudleigh* which were tactfully repulsed to render her a greater favourite of the Princess.

However much Elizabeth may have wished to take part in the orgies at Leicester House in preference to a quiet

*In the eighteenth century the word 'Mrs' prefixed the name of maids and matrons alike.

game of piquet with the Princess or a dreary circle of her equally bored companions when called in attendance to their tambour frames; or to a musical evening of a trio twanging a harp, squeaking on the violin and playing the harpsichord, she showed no sign that such entertainment was as boring to her as to her sister Maids.

More and more did the Princess, a self-effacing nonentity, rely upon Elizabeth for companionship. Brought up in the strict German Court of one of the lesser princes, and scandalized at the promiscuous intrigues of the Maids of Honour, Augusta turned to the only one of her attendants whom she knew to be loyal and, apparently, chaste.

At last Elizabeth, after discarding other and less eligible suitors, became desired in marriage by the Duke of Hamilton — which few of them offered, despite their avowed adoration for her.

A Duke! Nothing lower than a Duke would have won the much-desired Mistress Chudleigh, nor did she require the encouragement of Her Royal Highness to accept him who could have been but a toddler when Elizabeth while living at Chelsea had been the playmate of his elder brothers whom he succeeded to their father's dukedom. He was at least five years her junior and still in the care of a tutor shortly to accompany him on the Grand Tour that in those days all young gentlemen of quality were bound to undertake.

He fell violently in love with her and she, if less in love with him than with his dukedom, responded to his ardour with moderate restraint; for while she held him at arm's length she realized that her reticence would only add fuel to the fire of this, his first love. That it was calf love she guessed, and looked ahead to the outcome of such a marriage and, putting aside the social advantage to be gained by it, she had doubts that it might prove to be a failure, not on her part but on his.

Elizabeth's tentative opposition to Hamilton's advances may have been induced by the thought that what he hoped to find in her were the fruits of her experience. In a Court of hedonistic disregard for the chastity of women, where marriage vows were made to be broken by example of the King and his son, it could not have occurred to the fledgeling Hamilton that this lovely Maid of Honour was as virginal as himself. Nor did she disillusion him when he came to her distraught after her first guarded refusal. She was in truth a virgin, for she guessed that her chances of the grand match she and her mother had envisioned would be enhanced in a society where the word 'virgin' was a euphemism.

Stammering, pleading, he raved that he loved her, would love none other while he lived – could she not believe him? He could not believe *her* – that she was entirely indifferent – or else why had she given him that small hope – to wait?

'Wait!' he cried. 'You said I must wait – a month – for your answer. It has been an eternity. Am I repulsive to you? Are there others? There must have been others – lovers – there's not a Maid of Honour here in Court who could have had . . . how many have you had? I w-wouldn't care! I know I'm not the first so long as I could be the last. . . .'

He was on his knees to her, his young face blanched with the white-heat of his passion. His delicate slender-fingered hands felt feverishly to clutch at hers.

'Will you not mer-marry me? What have you against me? Am I too young?' He had heard – who had not? – of the infatuation of Pulteney for her, how through his influence she had been brought to Court, and he had learned enough from his Aunt Lady Archibald Hamiliton, to embellish the rumour that Pulteney's interest in the lovely Mistress Chudleigh was anything by fatherly. . . . 'Too young, am I,' he repeated it with old Pulteney in mind, 'too young for you?'

'No.' She was stirred, her hand stroking back a fallen lock of the fair hair astray on his forehead. He wore no wig, was unpowdered, looked even younger than his years, 'but I am too old – for you.'

'Too old!' He sprang to his feet, his face now flushed with heated denial. 'You – you are not much older than I. Anyway, what is age? Must you trifle with me? You – old!' A harsh laugh escaped him, he was bordering on hysteria. 'Would I want a missish, milk-and-water girl of my own age or younger? 'Tis you, you – *you* I want for my wife to – to have and to hold now and for ever.'

He had shattered her defences; her scruples as to the few years difference in their ages fled with the breath of her body, and the colour from her face. He was terribly in earnest, so desirous and – desirable. None of those others who had vowed eternal love for a day, a week, a month and then – to pass her by for more intimate game than the standoffish, thus far and no farther 'Maid Chudleigh', had roused her as did this boy who, seeing her melting, gathered her into his arms; a boy grown to manhood in a second between seconds. His hot eager mouth on hers, she yielded to his long stormy kiss with a passion that more than uttered words convinced him she was his 'now and for ever'. . . .

They exchanged vows and rings and things after she had extracted a promise from him to keep their betrothal a secret. She still had her doubts if he, so young, scarcely nineteen and about to leave for the Grand Tour, would remain hers 'for ever' should he meet with another more youthful and equally desirable. In which case she had no fancy to be labelled 'jilted' for the whole Court to know that Hamilton had been 'snaffled', as her sister Maids put it in smiling spite laced with envy, 'to ride an unbroken colt holding the whip hand and his Dukedom along with his twenty thousand a year, whether seventeen and not seven years older than he, for God alone knew her age which she always kept dark'.

Elizabeth, ignoring whispers meant for her ears, held her head high as if it already bore the ducal coronet upon it, saw her 'unbroken colt' take his departure for the Grand Tour, he in tears and she near to them, for by this time she had really come to love him, and had he shown he was ready to take her she would have let herself be taken before they could be man and wife. It may have been somewhat to her chagrin that he cared too much for her fair name not to seal his vows of 'eternal love' with a bond that would have compelled him to bring their secret betrothal to its legitimate end in wedlock before his departure.

So off on the Grand Tour went the enamoured Duke, and she to the country thankful for a change from the gossiping Court and constant attendance on the Princess. Her future assured, she was free to take a holiday with the approval of the Princess, who had been confided with her Maid's secret. 'But I am sad for my sake,' sighed Augusta, 'dat I am to loose you, even for dis so small a time who must loose you when you marry.'

For if married, a Maid of Honour must forfeit her position; it was an unwritten law that she must be a maid in fact as well as in name. How many of the young women were entitled to that distinction was doubtful. At least two were known to have retired to 'the country' where they had been delivered as the result of too close an intimacy with the anonymous father of the infant.

When Elizabeth also retired to 'the country' to stay with an aunt, rumour was rife again.

Mrs Hanmer, her mother's widowed sister, lived at Lainston House near Winchester. It was not her own house; she lodged with a Mr Merrill, a cousin of Colonel Chudleigh. Unlike Mrs Chudleigh, although equally impoverished, she had not married into the same courtly sphere. Her subsequent interference with the splendid marriage arranged between her niece and Hamilton can only be accounted for by a long nurtured jealousy of her sister's higher social position. Her daughter Elizabeth, a favourite of the Princess of Wales and in the course of a year or two likely to become a Duchess, may have contributed to Mrs Hanmer's activities not only in the breaking of this engagement but of sponsoring another to end in disaster for her niece.

However that may be, Elizabeth having unwisely, perhaps a trifle boastfully, told her secret to her aunt and that the duke would be writing to her continuously while on his tour, Mrs Hanmer felt it her duty to nip this romance in its bud.

The Duke of Hamilton, she told her conscience that may somewhat have painfully pricked her, could not honestly intend to marry Elizabeth if, as she surmised, he had taken all he wanted from the girl – a girl no longer in her middle twenties. Mrs Hanmer had heard of the famous Maids of Honour and of their scandalous private, if not always public, lives. She discussed her suspicions with Mr Merrill, a pompous, lean-minded old ass, who entirely agreed that Elizabeth should be saved from an obvious philanderer who might already have done his worst by her and with no intention to right his wrong, whatever might be his promises. 'No! never let it be said that a Chudleigh,' which Mr Merrill was not, being related on the distaff side to the late Governor of Chelsea Hospital, 'should be betrayed into a sin that is worse than death.'

All of which was balm to Mrs Hanmer's conscience when she took upon herself to intercept the letters that arrived re-addressed from the Court and bearing the seal stamped with a ducal coat of arms.

The letters, vowing passionate love and adoration were read and their contents registered, as never the letters of an honest lover, such absurdly exaggerated outpourings of Love! 'Methinks the gentleman doth protest too much!' was the obvious conclusion to be drawn from them and duly reported to Mr Merrill.

22

'Destroy them,' was his advice, 'and find her a husband who will do the right thing by her – and hastily too. There may not be much time! She looks peaked in my opinion.'

And in Mrs Hanmer's opinion she did look peaked, 'which could – God forbid – suggest –'

A suggestion mutually left unfinished, but their meaning was clear enough.

Elizabeth in a rare state was torn between doubt and fear that he to whom she had bound herself with exchange of rings and vows had proved faithless. And she now most truly loved him, his dukedom but a secondary consideration since in this case absence had certainly made *her* heart grow fonder. Not one letter! Not a word, no sign, no message – he could at least have sent a message by the Court courier. The Princess sent her messages by him, not the King's messenger but the Prince's own messenger. Was he ill or – gracious heaven, not dead? The smallpox. In the Courts of Europe there would be smallpox everywhere. . . . Yes, he was dead. He *must* be dead or he would have written unless – a more dreadful fear possessed her – unless he regretted his promise, had found another girl to supplant her. Some French or Italian beauty. He would be welcomed at any foreign Court and he was young, not very much younger than herself but – younger.

Each day dragged by while she waited and she waited; and Mrs Hanmer also waited, watchfully alert to take the post bag from Mr Merrill's footman and open it, rummaging for letters addressed to:

Mistress Chudleigh
Maid of Honour to Her Royal Highness
the Princess of Wales
at Leicester House,
London,
England.

Every one of these letters was as wormwood to Mrs Hanmer who read into each passionate word the ruin of her niece. . . . The fashionable hoop as worn by the *haut monde* with bunched panniers was specially designed to hide – the obvious.

As Elizabeth grew paler and more than ever 'peaked', her heart grown tender and warmer turned cold but not to freeze and break; she was not and never would be a sentimentalist yet just to crack, a very little.

From showering unwritten endearments upon him, for she had no address where to write, he having given her none (he would write, he had promised, from every halt upon his travels) she flung scorn at him for a lying hypocrite, 'to play fast and loose with me!' She rated herself high, her price in virtue of her enforced chastity higher than rubies, so high as a ducal coronet or higher if the Prince would be ensnared . . . No pimp at Court, silently she raged, pacing up and down her room, could so treat a doxy Maid of Honour – be damned to Honour! There's no honour at Leicester House. I'd have done better to lose mine than to be made his fool! So much for his promises of eternal love, down on his knees – a suckling. Wouldn't know how to use himself if I'd given him the chance had he the guts to ask it!

The gentle, modest, retiring Mistress Chudleigh could scarcely have been recognized by her Princess in the flaming virago who swore: 'By God Almighty, if he came crawling back to me I'd tell him where to take himself – to hell with him! If I'm befooled then I'll befool another. I'll take the first of any fool that offers . . .'

So in her wounded pride and the smarting hurt of besotted love, betrayed, forgotten, jilted – damn his soul! – did she swear; nor guessed that the first fool to offer was even then upon his way.

TWO

In July of that year H.M.S. *Cornwall* docked at Portsmouth and some of her naval officers attended the races
at Winchester. Mr Merrill, who enjoyed placing modest
bets upon his fancy, was accompanied by Mrs Hanmer
and Elizabeth.

It was a fashionable gathering with coaches and
carriages lined up along the barriers, their occupants
partaking of picnic luncheons on the steps of their
conveyances or on chairs placed by footmen while the
townsfolk were scattered on the grass eating oranges and
sandwiches and drinking ale from bottles: a motley crowd
interspersed with gipsies, bogus fortune-tellers and raucous-
voiced bookies even as on race courses today.

It was Elizabeth's first experience of a race meeting, as
the Princess of Wales cared nothing for the sport, but
Elizabeth, always a good horsewoman, was in her
element.

The sun glared down upon the turf and on the jockeys
in their varied colours leading their horses from the
paddock and mounted for the start. The modish gowns
of fashion, mingled here and there with gold-laced
uniforms, made a kaleidoscopic pattern against a fringe of
trees that edged the course.

'I declare,' exclaimed Mrs Hanmer, whose eyes were
everywhere, 'if that young gentleman,' she indicated a
group from *Cornwall*, 'is not Mr Hervey. You know –' she
nudged Mr Merrill, who had a telescope screwed to his
eye, watching the horses at the starting point and hopefully marking his choice – 'he is a younger son of that

Lord Hervey whom Mr Pope so wickedly attacked as "Lord Fanny".'

'Ah, yes,' Mr Merrill prided himself on his knowledge of current literature and the poets, ' "Let Sporus tremble What! That thing of silk, that mere white curd of asses' milk" – how goes it? – "Satire or sense, alas, can Sporus feel, who breaks a butterfly upon a wheel". . . Yes, neither John Hervey nor Lady Mary Wortley Montagu were spared Pope's vicious attack, these twenty or more years ago.'

But Mrs Hanmer had no ears for Mr Pope or his vicious attack upon Lord Hervey, he who had been Vice-Lord Chamberlain to His Majesty the King and had himself been the younger son of an earl.*

Mrs Hanmer would have no objection to an alliance of her sister's daughter with the younger son of a possible heir to earldom, and no likelihood of his ever attaining the peerage, as John Hervey had other sons to succeed him; but it may have slightly eased the still occasional pricks of her conscience in having prevented Elizabeth's marriage with a Duke if she could bring about a less exalted marriage with the grandson of an earl. It had not escaped her notice that Lieutenant Hervey – she observed the gold braid upon his sleeve that indicated the rank of a junior officer – had cast more than one look of evident interest on Elizabeth.

She, too, had seen that she had made an impression on this young officer whose appearance had much in his favour. Debonair, well set up and not too young for her. She had done with 'sucklings'.

Mrs Hanmer who had never, as had her enviable sister, even the most distant acquaintanceship with courtly circles, seized upon opportunity in her recognition of Lieutenant Hervey, he having been pointed out to her at

*John Hervey, whom Pope satirized, succeeded his brother, elder son of the Earl of Bristol, with the courtesy title of Lord Hervey.

a race meeting here at Winchester when *Cornwall* was docked at Portsmouth the year before.

Edging closer to the naval group from where she stood with Mr Merrill and Elizabeth, the enterprising Mrs Hanmer made bold to approach Mr Hervey and:

'Excuse me, sir,' said she (sketching a bob), 'Lieutenant Hervey, is it not? I had the pleasure of knowing your father, Lord Hervey, some few years ago.' This, of course, was a blatant fabrication, but Mrs Hanmer, a constant reader of the news-sheets concerning notabilities, had laid in a store of such items as might be of use to her should she ever meet with anyone connected with the Court or a title. So: 'You were but a child,' she made rapid calculation to extemporize, 'when I knew your father. Having long retired from the Court I have lost touch with my former associates.' This was safer ground since she did not know if his father were alive or dead. 'Pray, sir, as an old acquaintance of your father –'

'Not old, Madam,' he interrupted, gallantly bowing.

'Well, sir,' she simpered, 'not young as is my niece, Mistress Chudleigh, Maid of Honour to the Princess of Wales. She is on a visit to the, er, the country estate where I reside with my cousin, Mr Merrill. I was about to ask' – she had brought in tactfully her niece's appointment to further his interest already evinced in Elizabeth's direction – 'if you would care to partake of a cold *al fresco* collation with Mr Merrill, myself and my niece. Mr Merrill,' she enlarged, 'is an indefatigable patron of the Turf, a member and steward of the Jockey Club,' of which were neither Mr Hervey nor Mr Merrill. The Navy was seldom seen on any race course unless their ships were in port as now, within an easy ride from Portsmouth, and Mr Merrill had never owned a racehorse in his life.

'Madam,' another bow, 'I am honoured to accept your most kind invitation.' His eye had roved again towards Elizabeth, and not a little to the envy of his brother officers, who had not been invited to partake of 'a cold *al fresco* collation' with the prettiest girl within sight. Mr Hervey was walked away.

The face of Mrs Hanmer, beneath rather too youthful a hat graced with rosebuds atop an elaborately powdered 'head' arranged in a pyramid of curls, was wreathed in smiles to present the Honourable Mr Augustus Hervey, Lieutenant, Royal Navy, to:

'My niece, Mistress Elizabeth Chudleigh, and Mr Merrill of Lainston Hall,' which sounded grander than the not so very grand Lainston House. . . .

'Why, damme, ma'am,' remarked Mr Merrill after the luncheon and the races on which he had won two pounds and he, Elizabeth and Mrs Hanmer, well pleased with her manoeuvres, had driven back to Lainston House. Mrs Hanmer had ascertained that *Cornwall* would be at Portsmouth for the next three or four weeks, and she and Merrill discussed this meeting with Lieutenant Augustus Hervey. 'He,' said Mr Merrill, 'is evidently smitten with Elizabeth and if she plays her cards well enough, she'll hook him.'

'No need for her to play her cards,' was Mrs Hanmer's complacent reply to that, 'his cards are already on the table. His father,' she preened herself, 'is, or was, in high office at the Court and a friend – perhaps too intimate a friend –' she added pursing a lip, 'with Lady Mary Wortley Montagu. He may not be a Duke but Elizabeth will still be marrying into a titled family if she takes him.'

Would she take him?

Mrs Hanmer devoutly prayed so, for such a marriage would be more conformable to her taste if less to that of her sister, who had caused much heartburning envy to Mrs Hanmer, even if Mrs Chudleigh were no longer *persona grata* at the Court where her daughter was Maid of Honour; and Mrs Hanmer had learned that if a Maid of Honour were a wife she could no longer be in waiting

28

on the Princess of Wales or, as might come to be if Elizabeth aimed higher, on the Queen. Were she a Duchess such honour would have equally been forfeited, but in that case her social position would have suffered no loss. As the wife of a mere naval officer she would be deprived of her high social status and be nothing more than a – nobody. All this flashed through the mind of Mrs Hanmer when she informed her cousin Merrill:

'As Mr Hervey's ship will be in Portsmouth for the next month or so, I have invited him to dinner tomorrow.' Mrs Hanmer, a poor relation of the widowed Merrill, acted as his hostess and housekeeper in return for board and lodging which, added to the small stipend left her by her husband, gave her sufficient means to maintain her not too moderate requirements . . . 'Salmon soused in oporto,' she decided, 'followed by saddle of mutton, roast fowls and . . .' she made mental notes to instruct the cook, while Merrill said he would order the butler as to wines.

'They drink a-plenty aboard ship, and he shan't go short of my cellar's best.'

That dinner the next day preceded several more and were returned by an invitation from Mr Hervey to take the ladies over his ship under the command of Sir John Danvers. It is likely that the now greatly enamoured Lieutenant Hervey was proud to escort so pretty a Maid of Honour in H.M.S. *Cornwall*.

Elizabeth had given up all hope of Hamilton, and although her hurt pride was not yet entirely healed she found Hervey's advances went far to soothe the scar. Urged by her aunt she determined, should he offer, to take him as many other young ladies in similar case, before or since, have taken the first 'fool' who offered – on the rebound of a broken engagement.

On Hervey's fourth visit to dinner they walked in the garden at Lainston House. The westering sky glorified the pastures where cows grazed under pink-tinged clouds that heralded the last of the day's sun. Roses in fullest bloom drifted their fragrance on the warm soft air to mingle with the scent of new-mown hay; and birds chorused their evensong as accompaniment to Hervey's not unexpected avowal when, halting in the flower-bordered path, he came out with:

'Madam . . . Elizabeth . . . if I may so call you by your name . . .' He was flushed, his broken words poured from him clumsily. 'I . . . you must have seen that I want . . . I love . . . you. I . . . do you? Will you? I mean . . . marry me?'

She could hardly hold her giggles at so awkward a proposal, very different from the fervent declaration of young Hamilton. Feigning modest hesitation, she answered him:

'Sir, I am honoured and . . . and surprised that you should wish to marry one whom you have known so short a time.'

'Two weeks but . . . I wanted . . . I mean I . . . loved you at first sight. I know I am unworthy of you, so far above me in everything and . . . every way.'

Mrs Hammer had rubbed it well in that her niece held high position at the Court of the Prince of Wales, heir to the Throne and who, judging by the dissolute life his father led, might soon ascend it as King, when the Princess whom Elizabeth served would become Queen. This being possible at any time, as stressed by Mrs Hanmer, the favourite Maid of Honour although a maid no longer would have certain influence that might obtain for Mr Hervey the rank of Admiral of the Fleet!

Neither Elizabeth nor Mrs Hanmer, nor any other subject of George the Second could guess that the King would long outlive his son leaving his heir, a grandson still in the nursery, to succeed him.

'I have so little time,' continued Mr Hervey, gaining courage to pursue his declaration since she had not decidedly let him down to lead him on, 'before we sail that I had to tell you . . . if I . . . may hope?'

'I thought,' said she recovering her assumed discomposure and maidenly surprise, 'that your ship would be at Portsmouth for the next few weeks.'

'We have had orders to curtail . . . we are bound for the West Indies within the week, and so . . . Oh, pray, Mistress Chud . . . Elizabeth, I cannot risk to lose you . . . I may be away . . . we are at war . . . and any time, any day my ship may be in action against the French and . . . can we . . . will you take me if I dare aspire to so great an honour . . . that you will wed with me so soon as . . . if you are willing?'

She was willing enough to risk a hasty wedding that she might be sure of him lest no other should 'aspire'. For Hamilton's betrayal had cut deep, so let it rest and remain forgotten and herself avenged – on one condition: that the marriage should be kept a solemn secret for the present. Would he promise?

On his knees, as Hamilton before him, head bowed, he promised . . . 'If you will, although I'd wish to claim you mine before the world. I love you . . . I adore you . . .' He was on his feet to take and hold her close. She could hear the hurry of his heart and marvelled at his passionate possession of her mouth to amaze her, and she had thought him so bashful! He could, she told herself, compete in expertise with others who explored to take all except the final consummation, and to whom she had responded in so far as she had held herself intact.

Mrs Hanmer was delighted at the success of her activities to capture for her niece Lieutenant Hervey of a titled family but with no chance of his ever succeeding to the earldom of Bristol. As for the secret wedding, that too must be arranged and speedily. She knew sailors would swear fidelity to every girl at port of call, and then . . . away.

'So have him marry her,' said Mr Merrill, 'and I'll tell Amis to hasten with the banns and special licence that there'll be no delay. The *Cornwall* sails next Monday so on Saturday at the latest let it be.'

And this was Sunday.

On the night of 14 August 1744, the Reverend Mr Amis, Vicar of Sparsholt, was summoned to Lainston House where the wedding party, if party it could be called, was met to celebrate the marriage of the Hon. Lieutenant Augustus Hervey, Royal Navy, with Elizabeth Chudleigh, spinster. There was none present to witness the ceremony in the small chapel of Sparsholt village that stood in the grounds of Lainston House, other than Mrs Hanmer, Mr Merrill, and a friend of his, a Mr Mountenay.

Elizabeth, when begged by her lover to tell him why she insisted on this secrecy, explained, as she also had informed her Aunt Hanmer: 'I cannot remain a Maid of Honour if I am married. And I would not wish to renounce my position at Court because –' she gave this as her reason, which it wasn't, for she had no intention of severing so influential a connection with a future Queen of England to be the wife of an obscure naval officer with whom she was not in the least in love – 'because,' she raised him from sixth to seventh heaven by telling him, 'if I were no longer in attendance on Her Royal Highness I would have no power to gain for you the highest rank that you deserve.'

On that fatal August night they wandered hand in hand through the gathering dusk. The moon, with a halo of bronze around it, cast distorted shadows of a cedar on the lawn; and above it one ice-green star caught among the spreading branches winked eerily down to send a shiver through her spine.

'Are you cold, my dearest?' he asked tenderly.

'No, just – as my mother used to say – a grey goose walked over my grave.'

'Talk not of graves,' he shivered slightly too, 'except that I am all but dead in mine to think that I must leave you within three days of this.'

32

'This' was the wedding service conducted by Mr Amis in the little dark chapel. The only light to maintain entire secrecy as Elizabeth insisted was one candle set, of all places, in Mr Mountenay's hat!

Was ever woman in such fashion won or in such fashion wed?

A thin grey finger of dawn crept through a chink in the window curtains of the room allotted to the bridal pair with a powder closet adjoining, large enough to take a bed if needed; and it was. There she would sleep if another dreadful night must be passed with him – her husband. Yes, God help me, she screamed within herself, my husband!

On the pillow beside her he lay naked, for the night was warm and he uncovered. His face in that dim light showed her his mouth half open, emitting slow deep snores of satisfaction.

Her racked tormented body seemed no longer to belong to her, abased, its flesh in weals from ill-usage of his connubial rights. . . . His rights! Her mind reeled, striving to discard the horror of it disguised in tenderest beguilement of 'Love.' . . . Never, no *never* let me hear that word from him or any man again. 'I love you, my own lovely one.' He had torn her night shift from her to say: 'You are as I dreamed you when I saw you first under your woman's fripperies, so small and slender as a reed or a beautiful boy'. . . . Memory went searching to recall what Hamilton had told her when his young passion had stormed upon her throat, her breast, under her feminine fripperies' . . . 'I love your loveliness, so exquisitely slender, so different from the –' he grinned, mischievously quizzing '– the flamboyant bosomy opulence of women who flaunt themselves to pleasure the King and his odious son.' . . . Yes, she knew she was small and unfashionably slender for she had developed late and yet would run to plumpness to pleasure men who desired the 'flamboyant'. But not

33

this one here. No! Not he, tired of his normal lusts for women ... And she, unconsummated, was no innocent though ignorant of a husband's privilege, and were she mated to a man and not a beast, and worse than any natural beast, how gladly would she give him her virginity ... 'With my body I thee worship,' so had he pronounced that mockery of vows before the altar five hours since.

Her quivering closed eyelids lifted to see burnt low in their sockets the candles that had lighted them to bed. Propped against the wall she saw his riding whip, instrument of his perverted desire fulfilled ... And more awful than that, the hideous demanding of his marital rights to possess and take her how he would against her screaming protest, her face forced downward on the pillows while he ... God! she prayed, so let me die of this most dreadful shame ... !

She could not know of the predilections not only of certain of his shipmates and other men at sea who, for months or years in warfare, were denied the sight of women; but also in High Society it was not uncommon among her own associates. Nor did she heed nor perhaps had understood the tittered innuendos of her sister Maids nominating this one, that one, and Mr Hervey's own father, 'Lord Fanny' with his painted face, now grown old; he who had been the butt of Mr Pope whose *Imitations of Horace* Mr Pulteney, her elderly flame, had read to her while she yawned. And, as she remembered, they had giggled at the devilish things Pope wrote of Lady Mary although today he was considered to be the greatest poet of these times, yet sickly and might not live another year. ...

Her wandering thoughts recaptured her shocked reaction to this, her wedding night, and he, her husband – never, never, *never!* She dug her nails deep into her palm, never to be her husband. ... But how to be released? There is some such thing, she believed, as annul-

34

ment if proved, as she could be, intact and her maidenhead unbroken.

She must not pass another night with him under this roof or, if impossible to free herself without raising a hornet's nest of questions, reproaches, and his pursuit of her to drag her back and put her in the wrong, he who had done unutterable wrong to her. . . . No, not by that way of escape could she leave him. She must stay these two more days and nights until he sailed . . . and God send he may be drowned or killed in sea battle, as they were always at war with France or Spain or somewhere. And she would keep to her insistence of the secret wedding as arranged between them; he was agreeable to that, since he had no wish she should renounce her attendance on the Princess, with its promise of future preferment for him when the Prince of Wales became King.

Rosy morning light filtered through the curtains while still he slept, but she did not, save uneasily to doze from this waking nightmare, until Anne Craddock knocked at the door with her voice behind it saying:

'Madam, if you are wishful that I bring breakfast to you and Mr Hervey . . .'

Welcome relief from the long night's agony that had racked her nerves to breaking point.

'Yes, I will have breakfast brought to me – to us – at once.'

He woke, his mouth gaping wide. His eyes full of sleep gazed up at her where she raised herself to look with loathing down at him, while desire stirred in his quickened breath to tell her:

'No, not breakfast yet. I must enjoy you now, my dearest love, and then . . . again!'

He made as if to take her but she cried in muted frenzy:
'Anne! Yes, bring in the breakfast. We are ready for it.'

Saved! A seemly façade lowered on that hideous travesty of a marriage night which many years later

35

would be testified by that same Anne Craddock who had seen them in bed together, she so modest, he so deep in love.

And for the next two nights the wretched ruse was played. Elizabeth gave the unsuspicious Mrs Hanmer a not unnatural excuse that her 'flowers were upon her earlier than due, and this being so . . . if her aunt could have a bed brought to the powder closet for him because . . . you see?'

Aunt Hanmer saw with smiling nods. The same thing had happened to herself on the morning after her own wedding night with her late lamented. It was a case not unusual with a virgin bride. She applauded her niece's reticence. 'Of course a bed should be brought but she doubted' – more nods and smiles – 'he would take it.'

He didn't. Elizabeth made it clear to him when they were alone on the ensuing night, that:

'I will never while I live be your wife except in name. I hate you, I abhor you! Abomination that you are! No – don't touch me –' as he dragged her to him. She struggled, fighting with her fists, clawing to scratch his face, kicking at his shins in their fine white silken hose to draw an ooze of blood on each.

'Goddamn!' He fell apart from her, staring. 'Have you run mad?'

'Not I. 'Tis you are mad. A beast – to rot in hell with others of your kind. I will sleep here in the closet and you in this bed that you've fouled. But to save your face – and mine – I'll join you here for breakfast, a happy married couple wed in secret that I may keep my state – my honourable state –' A sob of hysterical fury strangled her words as she made to have at him again but that he caught her hands and would have dragged her to the bed, tearing at her night shift to unloose it, had not another timely interruption intervened. Anne with a steaming ewer. 'Hot water, Madam, for your basin' . . . (God be

36

thanked!) 'I have put a basin in the closet, sir,' said Anne, 'for your shaving water.'

She curtsied herself out.

'What in the devil!' He rushed to the closet, saw the bed made up and rounded on her fiercely. 'What in hell's name does this mean?'

'What I have said. I sleep in the closet, you here, but supposedly in the closet. All is explained to my aunt circumspectly. It is not unusual for a wife to have her flowers come upon her, hastened by excitement of her first marriage night.... No! Keep away! She smote the air as he approached, dodging his next attack and glancing apprehensively around to see if a weapon were handy. Her eyes were on the poker in the fireless grate. She dashed to get and seize it for defence as he came after her and she, holding him at bay, darted to the small adjoining room, banged the door and locked it. To make sure, she placed against it a heavy chair, the only other furniture except the dressing-table on which Anne had put a basin for his shaving water.

Because Anne, as confidential maid to Mrs Hanmer, was sworn to keep the marriage secret for the reasons given and accepted by Aunt Hanmer, Mr Merrill and the bridegroom, that Miss Chudleigh should remain a Maid of Honour, Elizabeth took breakfast the next morning in the nuptial room and in the nuptial bed.

'It is the custom among high society,' Mrs Hanmer told her abigail, 'for gentlemen of Quality to have a dressing-room at their disposal. It was remiss of me not to have arranged for the Lieutenant to have the powder closet for his use.'

And Elizabeth, in order to maintain the tragic farce, continued to take her breakfast with him in the bridal room and in the bridal bed. Nor did Mrs Hanmer, for her peace of mind, know of her niece's conniving to remove herself from further injury, as chronicled long afterwards by the anonymous author of the *Authentic details of*

Particulars relative to the Life of Elizabeth Chudleigh, in which we may delicately learn that '*the connubial rights were attended by consequences injurious to health as well as unproductive of fecundity; and from the night following the day on which the marriage was solemnized, Miss Chudleigh resolved never to have further connection with her husband.*'

If these 'Authentic Particulars' were told by Elizabeth who could and did vouch for them, we may likely believe them. We may also believe that when Hervey's two or three days' leave were up and he rejoined his ship, she had no more to do with him other than to keep up the pretence before her beaming aunt and Mr Merrill that there was never so happy and content a bride as she who could still take her place at Leicester House as Maid of Honour, which indeed she was if not in honour.

*   *   *

Elizabeth's return to Court after her visit to her aunt as a Maid in name, a wife in fact, could remain in attendance on the Princess Augusta of Wales. The scandals attached to the Maids of Honour at Leicester House were a byword both in and out of the Court; but never was the slightest evidence that Elizabeth's conduct had been other than most discreet. This much to her credit in that the gallantries of the Prince of Wales were notorious.

Elizabeth's rejection of Prince Frederick's advances did not extend to a complete indifference to the amatory approaches she received from a number of admirers, including the Duke of Ancaster, one of her former playmates at Chelsea. Yet she still preserved her distance as *demi-vierge*, 'thus far and no farther'.

Her secret wedding to Hervey was an ever-present menace to her peace of mind; and how often she may have regretted her moment of pique at Hamilton's apparent breaking of his betrothal vows of eternal love

38

and the loss to her of a dukedom, can only be conjectured.

What a crass besotted idiot was I, she in her privacy must have raged, to think she had not, at the time of his departure on the Grand Tour, announced their betrothal to everyone instead of urging him to secrecy, and then to take to herself the (unmentionable) Hervey.

That she was now in her twenty-fifth year and a spinster, which in those days of early marriages could be considered an 'old maid', gave rise to some comment among the other not so maidenly Maids. But the Princess attributed her rejection of marriage as devotion to herself and her desire to be ever in attendance, unmarried, upon Her Royal Highness. Augusta, while appreciating her motive in preserving her position as Maid of Honour that, if married, must perforce be discontinued, urged her 'not', as she gave it, 'to keep you from ze amusements and gaities of ze Court. Pleass to pleass me, *mein Hertz*, enjoy yourself at ze balls and masquerades. Even if I' (poor, insignificant Augusta who chose to live her monotonous life in her own apartments listening to doleful music, playing piquet with her uninterested Maids) – 'even if I do not care for ze dancing and masques, zere is no reason why you, my dear, should not.'

Given this permission, Elizabeth took full advantage of it. We hear of her at every ball and party held at the Court, and at Vauxhall or Ranelagh with a train of devotees at her heels, but always preserving the utmost decorum.

We also hear of her, and for the first time as the subject for the gossip that ever afterwards pursued her, at an hilarious dinner party in Leicester House which the Princess did not attend. It was on the occasion during the '45 Rebellion when the Young Pretender had captured Carlisle and was marching south.

Unlike many of his father's subjects, Frederick did not

39

much concern himself with this attempted invasion on the part of the rightful heir to the Throne. He turned the affair into an orgy to celebrate the expected failure of Charles Edward to claim his right, even though he had almost the whole of Scotland behind him.

Frederick had ordered an enormous cake designed in the shape of the fortress at Carlisle; and when it was brought to table the company bombarded it with sugar plums intended to represent the guns of the Scots. By this time the Prince and half the guests had drunk enough to render them merry and Frederick, merriest of all, bethought him to play a huge joke on the new Cabinet that had recently superseded what was known as the 'Leicester House' Government. Frederick particularly disliked Pitt, afterwards Lord Chatham, whose second son, Pitt 'the Younger', would later become one of the greatest Prime Ministers in the history of British politics to be jeered at as 'a sight to make surrounding nations stare, a kingdom trusted to a schoolboy's care'.

The joke now played upon the Cabinet by the heir to the Throne his grandfather had usurped (not, let it be said, of the late King's desire since George the First loathed England as much as England loathed him) was a decision of Frederick, now deep in his cups, to appoint Mistress Chudleigh as Secretary of War. This post he declared she would fill more efficiently than could Mr Pitt.

Commanding pen and paper the Prince dictated to the considerably discomfited Elizabeth, upon whom his eye was blearily fixed, a letter to Lord Harrington, Secretary of State, to draw up a warrant appointing Mistress Chudleigh to the post of Secretary of War.

Loud was the applause from the gentlemen, somewhat less from the ladies, as about fourteen of the unsteady male diners crowded to the head of the table when called by the Prince to sign the letter to Lord Harrington. Of course nothing came of what was indulgently regarded as a royal prank, but it served to increase the envy of

40

the other Maids who had not been chosen for this supposedly signal honour.

Elizabeth had now all to do to avoid the Prince's
attentions, yet she was never to be lured by his kindliest
leers into losing the favour of his wife.

While she had striven to put Hervey as much out of
her mind as out of sight, far away with the Mediterranean
Fleet, she kept well in touch with news of the Navy and
was appalled to learn that some of the ships were in the
Channel kept in port by foul winds. God send, she prayed,
his ship is not among them.

It was.

In January 1747 Hervey wrote to her. He had heard
of the success she enjoyed as the most desirable Maid
of Honour at the Leicester House Court and, as noted
by a contemporary, 'every butterfly fluttered around
her'.

On receipt of his letter insisting upon a reunion, Elizabeth fell into apprehensive frenzy. This shock in the
shape of Hervey's letter demanding a private interview
made her the more fiercely determined to resist him. He
hung about the gates of Leicester House in order, he
hoped, to waylay her, but the moment she sighted him
when driving by in the carriage placed at her disposal by
her mistress, she bade the coachman drive on and almost
ran down the persistent Hervey under the horses' hooves.

Eventually, for the time being, he gave up the chase
with a letter containing a menace that 'You have not seen
or heard the last of me.'

For a month or two Elizabeth had suffered torment
from Hervey's continuous letters imploring her to let
bygones be bygones or else – and this was awful – if she
did not comply with his desire to renew their marital
relations he would reveal their marriage to the world and
– the Princess!

The reason for Hervey's determination to claim her as
his wife and so end this interminable secrecy of her

choice, not his, was nothing more nor less than jealousy. He knew her to be the centre of attraction with other men who enjoyed, as he believed, the sexual intimacies denied to him, his lawful rights. That by his outrageous conduct on their wedding night he had forfeited such rights did not occur to him, goaded almost to madness by her determination to exclude him to whom she was legally bound, from a resumption of their marital relationship.

But his constant threats of exposure weakened her resolution never to communicate with him except by the written word. She realized that Hervey's persistence would finally end in her surrender and that must mean an end to her successful reign at Court and her devoted attendance on the Princess whom she had come to love; she who, even as her mistress, had been devoid of love in all her adult life. She discounted Hamilton believing he had deceived her into loving him.

She was at that time living in a rented house in Conduit Street. This street took its name in the eighteenth century from the conduit that ran through a large field, the site of the future New Bond Street, and looked to the north-west towards Tyburn Gallows, where its victims with all the barbarous horrors of disembowelling, could be seen trundled on hurdles past her windows. Not the most salubrious of views, but because it adjoined Hanover Square, named in honour of the first King George and built in 1720, it was a fashionable residence for a Maid of Honour.

Mrs Chudleigh looked after the house for her daughter and, as was currently assumed, may have accommodated a guest as in earlier hard-up days. Nor did she evince much curiosity concerning any of the gentlemen who called to see Elizabeth, save one, consistently refused admittance. 'Who,' she wished to know, 'is the young man who calls so often and whom Pompey' (Elizabeth's negro page) 'always tells you are not at home?'

42

'He pesters me beyond endurance,' was the answer and, in effect, the truth. 'He is a naval officer whom I met at the races when staying with Aunt Hanmer. He is nobody of importance.'

This sufficiently satisfied her mother who knew, as did everyone else, that Elizabeth was in great demand with suitors of the nobility, but the wonder and vexation of Mrs Chudleigh as to why her daughter should remain unmarried when she could pick and choose a husband from the peerage caused continuous friction between them. Yet Elizabeth would never divulge her secret to her mother for fear of creating more rows. Mrs Chudleigh had set her heart on Elizabeth's marriage with an earl at least, and that she should, seemingly, refuse the opportunity of marrying a peer, even if it meant forfeiting her position in attendance on the Princess of Wales, certain before long to be Queen, exacerbated the ambitious mother past all reason.

Meanwhile Hervey haunted the house in Conduit Street and continued to be furiously jealous to see other men permitted entrance but never himself. Each time he presented his card at the door he was told by the little black page, 'the ladee not at 'ome'.

Then one day, when he had ascertained that his wife's mother was away, 'my bloody mother-in-law – yes, damme!' he fumed to his inner man – having seen her drive off in a hired post-chaise with a pile of luggage and judged her to be gone to their Devonshire house which she visited from time to time – he forced an entrance.

He had already made inquiries at the local tavern frequented by footmen of the neighbouring houses that Mrs Elizabeth Chudleigh kept no resident staff; they were provided with lodgings near by and worked at irregular hours. None but her black boy was in constant attendance. She favoured the fashion of having about her always a little negro page. To the usual reply with which the page had been well primed, Hervey shoved the boy aside and

43

strode past him to a room at the end of the hall which his sleuthlike prowling had identified as his wife's parlour. Flinging open the door he saw her seated at a bureau writing a letter. To whom, he asked himself, jealousy mounting as she sprang to her feet, her cheeks ablaze.

'Who let you in?' she demanded. 'I gave orders you were never to be admitted.'

'I let myself in. You should employ a prize-fighter if you want to keep me out.' He turned at a sound of blubbering.

'What,' she cried, 'have you done to the child?' and made a dash for the door he had closed, saying as she opened it to see the boy with his knuckles in his eyes. 'Get out of my house! You have no right here.'

'I have every right and I shall prove it – here and now!'

There was no mistaking his meaning; his face hot with desire seeing her at these close quarters, for since their marriage night he had sighted her only at a distance, and he realized how much more desirable she was after these two years' absence.

Thoroughly alarmed, she rushed to the door but in one stride he was before her to lock the door behind him.

'Don't look at me as if I were about to kill you,' he said with a laugh, his arms stretched out to take her. 'I only want my rights as your husband.'

She darted away from him. 'I'd rather you did kill me!'

'My own dear love,' he advanced upon her, 'Why so harsh – unloving? One of your letters in return to mine gave me to think you are willing to –'

'Willing to –' it was her turn to laugh on a shrill hysterical outburst – 'willing to see you *hanged*!'

Dusk was falling and the watchman's voice outside in the street proclaimed 'Seven o' the clock and full moon rising.' It was late September and the days had shortened.

'Yes!' she ran to the window, pointing, 'there goes the empty hurdle that has taken one of your kind to Tyburn where *you* should be dangling!'

'A charming welcome from my bride,' he came to her again and this time caught and held her. 'For you are still my bride – my *lawful* bride.'

'No!' she screamed as he dragged her up to him, forcing his mouth on hers. She bit his lips, kicking at his shins as before when he had attempted to assert his 'rights'.

'I hate – I loathe you! I'd sooner die than have you do to me what not even a whore would suffer.'

But he was lost to all save his want of her. 'I've known whores,' he muttered thickly, 'who've enjoyed it and at a cheaper price.'

'You filthy beast!'

But the more she raged the more he would have that for which he hungered.

He had pulled her to a couch and was unfastening his breeks while she, still screaming, called for 'Pompey! Fetch the watchman – the constable!' But the boy had fled to his quarters, scared at the yells of his 'Madahm' and fearing himself to be a victim of attack from the gentleman who had knocked him down in his haste to reach the lady – for what purpose the ten-year-old – no innocent – could guess. He knew from talk below stairs that gentlemen whose blood – and 'it' – was up would stay at nothing unless the lady were willing.

That she was definitely *not* willing may be assumed from her account of the meeting which in after years she grimly related as 'an assignation with a vengeance'.

The 'vengeance' being, as the *Authentic Particulars* gives it, was 'the addition of a boy to the human race'.

If Hervey were so decisively dismissed by her we can only guess when – again we quote from the *Particulars* – 'he felt himself to be the Lord Paramount over a defence-less woman whose hopes he had blasted, whose person he had defiled'. That she refused ever to see or hear from him after this vengeful 'assignation' is positive; and that her return immediately to Court curtailing her leave from attendance on the Princess was the result of it.

He, too, the 'Lord Paramount', now promoted to Captain, returned to his ship on shorter leave than he had expected, for *Cornwall* was ordered to rejoin the Mediterranean Fleet and to sail again for the West Indies. He left his 'Lady Paramount' to resume her duties at Court with her secret marriage still unfolded; yet it required all her courage and adroitness to avoid the suspicion that three months later became a certainty.

How, she asked herself a hundred times, could this ever have come to her after what was no less than rape? While the women's gowns of that period could conveniently disguise her condition with voluminous hoops and panniers, after six months of pregnancy and at the advice of Caesar Hawkins, the Court surgeon, she was ordered 'a change of air' owing (tactfully) to her 'debilitated state of health!' Mr Hawkins had learned tact in dealing with the 'debilitated health' of the Maids of Honour at Leicester House and would often order 'change of air'.

'You gif too mooch of your time to me, *mein Hertz*,' said the Princess, when with humble apologies Elizabeth reported the surgeon's advice. 'But *naturlich* you must have a rest from your duties here mit me. Always in attendance when you be not so. Now go, my dear, and stay away from Court in the country. I vill miss you but you must do as the goot Mr Hawkins tells you.'

So off she went with the blessings and goodwill of Princess Augusta, who would indeed sadly miss the one and only faithful attendant on whom she could rely and who so assiduously rejected the Prince, her husband's, overtures.

Elizabeth chose for some reason or other, probably for its nostalgic memories, to take a villa at Chelsea. She took with her as sole attendant Anne Craddock. Her Aunt Hanmer, who, as Elizabeth never ceased to remind her, was partially if not wholly responsible for her marriage to

Hervey, reluctantly permitted Anne to accompany her to Chelsea.

'You must have known,' she stormed to her wilting aunt, 'why I had to keep up the pretence that all was well between us – and how I loathe and detest him!' She had refrained from divulging to her aunt details of the shame and degradation she had suffered on that fatal night. 'And you knew our wedding must be secret if I can keep my place at Court, so that I am still to all intent and purpose – God help me! – a maid – Maid of Honour . . . Honour!' A rasping laugh escaped her. 'What honour is here?' She laid a hand against her body. 'I never wanted *this* from him.'

'He is your husband,' said her aunt, weakly striving to excuse herself, knowing she had deliberately intercepted the letters from Hamilton inducing her niece to believe she had been jilted. 'Hervey was only asserting his rights. You should be overjoyed to bear his child. And,' she continued still in self-excuse and as a sop to the conscience pricks that came to her with every word from Elizabeth, 'he was and is in love with you. And you were ready enough to accept him.'

No use in further argument when what Aunt Hanmer had to say concerning her acceptance of Hervey was the truth for which she had so dearly paid. As for Hamilton – be damned to him and all men! She inwardly raged when she took herself and Anne off to Chelsea.

She was thankful that the ducal houses on the Thames were, in this height of the Court season, unoccupied by their owners as was also that of the late Sir Robert Walpole, the former Prime Minister who had died two years before in '45, just after Prince Charles Edward's attempted invasion. For the Stuart Prince, whom loyalists toasted as 'the King over the water', Elizabeth held an unuttered adherence. Despite his reputation as profligate and drunkard he was for her the rightful King of England and Great Britain. Certainly a better King, she would tell herself, than these guzzling lecherous Germans, disgustedly reminded of Prince Frederick's promiscuous adulteries.

Anne did not remain with her for more than a few weeks. Mrs Hanmer required her services, so Elizabeth was left to the care of strangers.

As her time drew near she dared not visit, as she longed to do, the hospital, lest some of the remaining veterans who had known her as a child and young girl would recognize her condition, now impossible to conceal. The servants who attended the villa had been told that the lady's husband was at sea, and it would be doubtful if he could return before her lying-in.

During the days preceding the birth, which she dreaded and frequently prayed that she, or it, would die in its deliverance, she would wander alone through the country lanes, so familiar to her in the past. It was midsummer and the trees and hedges turning from the bright and joyous green of June to the darker spinach green of July. Blackberries, shed of their flowering, offered their unripened fruit. She remembered how in a Devonshire lane she had been picking blackberries when Pulteney had come riding through the woods to hail her as a 'divinity' . . . Pulteney! Now Earl of Bath who had sunk into obscurity, he who had endeavoured to cultivate her mind with possible access to her body . . . Men! How she detested them and *this* that she carried so weightily, the result of Hervey's lust. . . . She had no wish to live. My life, she said, is hell. Were I a Catholic I'd believe I was having my purgatory here and not hereafter.

Then, on one of those daily walks, she was taken with the agonizing approach of the birth she had so miserably dreaded . . . Staggering along with none in sight she came to the villa on the outskirts of the village. A maidservant found her on the doorstep of the house. 'Fetch,' she managed to articulate, 'the doctor.'

The maid hurried; a doctor, or rather the village apothe-

48

cary, was sent for, and while Elizabeth lay in her travail, she told him: 'Send for Mr Caesar Hawkins. He knows me, I must have him attend me.'

The young apothecary was impressed by the name known to all the medical profession. Yet although Hawkins hastened by post-chaise as soon as the message reached him and was just in time to see the child born, his assistance was not necessary.

Leaning over the exhausted mother whose latest addition to the human race was sturdily announcing his disgust at being forcibly ejected from the comfortable cavern that for nine months had been his home and, at the top of his lungs, objecting to the midwife's ablutions,

'Miss Chudleigh,' portentously pronounced Mr Hawkins, who had not yet been told of her marriage state, 'you have a son.'

Later when they brought him to her and placed him in her arms, still yelling lustily – ''tis his food 'e wants, ma'am,' said the midwife. 'Bless 'is precious 'eart.'

Food! From her whose breasts were heavy laden with nourishment for Hervey's son! . . . Revolting.

But even as she held him, offering herself to his dribbling lips that suckled so greedily, a wave of overwhelming tenderness engulfed her as she gazed down upon his baldness where some fair hair was already sprouting. Red, crumpled, hideous, a squirming atom cradled in her arms, he was for her a gift from heaven. She, as all mothers from time immemorial, yearned over him as with the adoration of the Magi. . . .

'Mine,' she whispered when, his demands appeased, he gurgled contentment, subsided and slept . . . 'How could I ever have not wanted you? Mine! My all. My angel. I love you, love you, love . . .' she devoured his baldness with kisses, loth to detach his guzzling mouth from her nipple.

'Don't wake 'im, madam,' she was ordered by her who, stout, bustling, efficient, had borne eight of her own and

49

brought three times as many into the world. 'Let 'im sleep. And you too, ma'am. It was a lovely birth. I wish all could be so easy.'

'Easy!' Elizabeth echoed and thought, recalling the tortures of the damned – but oh, so well worth it for this! . . . 'If mine were easy what is difficult?'

'Lying wrong side up, dear,' and she added, relishing importance, 'some of 'em, mother an' child, dies if wrong side up or feet first, or else born dead. I've known as many as five stillborn and four with umps.'

'Umps?' fearfully queried. 'What are umps?'

'Umps, dear. Ump backs, from feet first.'

'Oh, no!' with a terrified glance at her somnolent angel.

'Not 'im, dear. 'E's perfect. Strong as an 'orse. And you too in your labour. I've known as many'll take forty-eight hours an' yours was only three.' She looked at the clock on the mantelshelf. 'I'll just be takin' a lay down for a while an' you too, ma'am, 'ave a sleep. I'll leave the door open so's you can call if I'm wanted. What a pity 'is Papa ain't 'ere to see 'im, but 'e'll be back from sea any time now.'

She bustled herself out . . . Three hours, said Elizabeth, adoring her son who cared nothing for her more than his necessary requirements . . . Three hours! Our Lord suffered three hours too, yet how much more worth it was His torture than mine that gave me you! And He suffered to save all of us, even I, wretched sinner that I am, but you are born in wedlock. God bless you . . . I must have you christened, my angel, but what am I to do with you? I can't take you to Court unless I acknowledge my marriage to your beast of a father, and even then I couldn't have you with me in attendance on the Princess because I'd be barred from being Maid of Honour. You'll have still to be my divine secret for I've not enough money to keep you as you must and shall be kept unless I remain at Court. I'll save every penny I earn to find you a home, but how can I part with you? And with whom can I leave you? Your father 'home from sea any time'? God forbid!

She was in greatest trouble now. Only Anne Merrill and her Aunt Hanmer knew of her marriage and this 'divine' result of it. Should she take him to Aunt Hanmer? No. Never to that old bitch! It's through her I met Hervey, but if I hadn't met him I wouldn't have had you, my treasure . . . What's to do?

What indeed to do?

Mr Hawkins was consulted by letter for he did not come again to see Elizabeth until after the christening that took place at the Church in Chelsea where Henry Augustus Hervey was baptized. On inquiry from Hawkins in consultation with the apothecary, a foster mother who lost her baby at the same time as Henry Augustus was born, had been found, and after all arrangements had been satisfactorily concluded, and the cottage which would be the temporary residence of Elizabeth's son, she, with torment more agonizing than his birth, was forced to leave her 'treasure' in another woman's care.

'I'll love him as my own, ma'am,' she was assured by the childless mother who told her: 'Three years wedded and my baby born dead – the only one,' sobs choked her as she took Henry Augustus from his mother's arms. 'And his father killed in sea battle never to know he was born. I wrote to his commanding officer but I doubt me he will ever get the letter. I wrote to the Admiralty, and now my husband will never come back.'

'I'd no such luck,' said Elizabeth: but this she did not say aloud. What she did say with genuine compassion for the young widow was:

'May *my* only one compensate you for your loss. I give – no, I lend him to you until I can have him back again as I have yet no home for him. Take this which will be sent to you every month in gratitude for your care of him.'

Four golden guineas were handed to her.

'I'd not take a penny, ma'am,' she was tearfully told, 'just for the love of him which I promise he will have, but so's he can be given every comfort.'

'I'll come and see him as often as I can,' said Elizabeth, also in tears, 'when not in attendance on the Princess of Wales.'

This was the first the woman had heard that her foster baby was the son of a Court lady, whether married or not, for she too, as had so many of the general public even as far from London as Chelsea, knew of the 'goings on' at the King's and the Prince's Courts. Still holding Henry Augustus, clamouring for nourishment, she curtsied.

'I'm honoured, ma'am, to nurse one so 'ighly born.'

'No more highly born than was your baby, my dear, for he, too, is the son of a sailor. . . . Let me feed him, just for the last time.'

And after having satisfied the immediate demands of Henry Augustus, Elizabeth broken-heartedly took her leave of him and drove in the carriage that awaited her return to Leicester House.

* * *

The welcome, with gushful *Schwärmerei* from the Princess at the reappearance of her favourite Maid of Honour, was accompanied by bantering innuendoes on the part of Elizabeth's sister Maids concerning her absence on account of 'ill-health' and the advice of Mr Hawkins – 'who, my dear Chudleigh,' with smiling spite remarked one Mistress Elizabeth Ashe, 'is always so careful of our well-being.'

'He is paid to be,' sweetly rejoined her dear Chudleigh, 'as you have good reason to know.' And as all the Court knew of this young person's retirement to the country on the careful advice of Mr Hawkins. But Mrs Ashe was an ever-present target of gossiping scandal, for which she cared not a pin, being more inclined to boast of her frolic-some escapades and the Prince's avuncular rather than amorous indulgence to her whose mother was the daughter of the King, Princess Amelia Sophia and sister of the Prince of Wales. Her father, so rumour had it, was the gallant – as fair in love as in war – Admiral Rodney.

But Elizabeth could hold her own and turn a disdainful back on the lot of them and their much-discussed suspicions conerning her or her companion's 'ill-health'.

The witty Lord Chesterfield was currently supposed to have answered her when she told him with an impudent uplift of her charming tip-tilted nose: 'My lord, do you know that the world says I've had twins?'

To which his twinkling lordship replied:

'Does it, madam? For myself I make it a rule only to believe *half* the world says.'

At which Elizabeth crowed with laughter; she could always enjoy and bear no grudge against a jest at her expense if it came from a noble peer; and her love of a title as great as her craving for money was not for herself but to support her son. From Hervey she realized she could expect neither a title nor pecuniary advantage. She was, however, not averse to accepting gifts of valuable jewellery and trinkets from her devotees, to be sold to the bearded gentlemen of St Mary Axe if occasion demanded, as it often did, to secure for her baby his extra needs. Also she acquired a taste for faro and other games of chance in which her many admirers allowed her to win their hundreds of guineas in the hope of favours to come and which still were barred as 'thus far and no farther'.

'To break the chastity belt of our self-blockaded Chudleigh,' as one of her followers put it, 'reminds me of the Turk who chased after his wives with a corkscrew having suspected a fellow of climbing in at the window of the harem.'

But no such chase, whether or not to break her chastity, was permitted by Elizabeth, and gossip again ran riot.

'With every man after her why does she choose *not* – to choose?'

Then to her dismay, albeit mingled with joy since she had always cherished in her heart her young first love, Hamilton was back from his Grand Tour and again at her feet, passionately ardent as ever.

We may believe that when he was received in her apartment at Leicester House the Court raised speculative eyebrows. He had not won her, it would seem, before he went away, but what now? Would she capitulate? Not for want of trying on *his* part, went word of it.

That meeting, as tactfully recorded in the *Authentic Particulars*: 'Occasioned emotions in the Duke which the heart can feel better than the pen can explain . . .' and must have resulted in a stormy scene that could be better explained as something in this wise:

'Why no answer to my letters? Did you deliberately deceive me, or was I only one of your numerous victims? After all your promises and your admission – dragged out of you I grant – that you – you cared for me, not to love, for I see you are incapable of love as I know and give to you!'

She saw he had grown to manhood in these two years since he had gone from her, never to return, as afterwards she had been led to persuade herself, for her undoing. Nothing of the 'suckling' was he now, purposeful, masterly to master her if she dared confess to him her marriage and obtain a divorce from Hervey were it possible. She had heard nothing of him since that last disastrous 'assignation'. Yet while she rejoiced to know that Hamilton had remained faithful, that he had never the remotest intention of breaking with her, that he loved and wanted her as wife and not mistress as did most of those others, not excluding the Prince of Wales. . . . All this and the possibility of divorce flashed through her mind and was dismissed as a hopeless impossibility, for were a divorce obtainable how could she account to the Princess for her blatant deception? And with Henry Augustus to prove it? Yes, he, her son, and more than any love she might be offered or prepared to take, *he* was her sole consideration.

She strove to steel her heart against Hamilton's desperate appeal imploring her to believe that he had written time and time again. . . . 'If you never received my letters,' urgent with love he seized her hands, crushing them, 'then some dastardly mischief has been done to intercept them. They can't all have gone astray. Other letters sent to his family by my tutor were received, so why not mine – especially as addressed to you at the Court?'

'Perhaps your tutor,' she essayed, even as the thought smote her that but one person only might have done this awful thing to destroy her life – 'Perhaps as you were in his charge and not then of age and –' hoping against hope that her suspicion as to the real culprit was unfounded – 'and he, your tutor, might have considered, and rightly so, that I was unsuited to be your wife and – Duchess,' her voice dwindled on the word that meant so much to her, more than her love for him, since it would have meant security for her beloved boy.

'My tutor! Do you think,' he shouted this at her, 'that he would have any influence with me as to my choice of the woman I want more than all else in the world and intended and *do* intend to marry? He, my paid servant!' The arrogant young dog! she thought, adoring him . . . O, this love, what is it? Rapture or torment? Why, she asked herself, down-glancing at him – he had knelt to her now, his head buried against her knees – why should one suffer so cruelly for love's sake?

He was saying distractedly:

'Who could have done this thing to me – to us – if what you tell is true, that you have never had my letters? Or are you lying to me?' He struggled to his feet, searching her face in fierce exasperation. 'Or are you trying to tell me that I am nothing to you now and never was? There is someone else? I'm supplanted – am I? Or is there a title higher than mine which would become you more? I

55

know – the whole world knows that our future King will bestow his filthy lust on any woman who'll respond to it and be given promise of nobility in her *own* right as his grandfather gave to his hideous German fraus! Is that what you would have?'

'I could almost disbelieve there is a God,' she spoke with icy calm, feeling as if every drop of blood in her veins had ceased to flow at this, his monstrous misconception of her avowal that his letters had never been received, 'that you could think I'd stoop myself as do those others, to gain such loathsome favour . . . No,' as he made to take her, contrite, 'save your breath. Even had your letters reached me,' she forced herself to say that which she knew would lose him and all hope of the love he craved, not as other men craved for her body to be paid for in the jewels she took from them for no return, only that her son should have the worth of them. 'Even then, had I received your letters,' she made her voice firm to say, 'I should have thrown them aside to join a heap of all such blather written by a herd of – calves! Did you honestly think that I, who can pick and choose my lovers where I will, would have wived me with a – calf?'

Scorn that stabbed to her innermost being was assumed to free her from this present hellish difficulty and so to scarify him that he would have none of her and be done with her . . . She was love-torn in tenderest pity for this youth whom she did most deeply want to care for her as wife – yes, as wife! cried her bruised soul who had never known wifehood with one whom she could love and not hate, while tears sight-blinded the look on his face at her lying words.

After a long pause: 'To do this to me!' he stood staring at her blankly, 'I, who have wasted all of me, my heart, my faith in women and my love, for I do – *did* love you. Why have we in our cursed English language no other word for love that can mean a dozen meaningless words for that which I, your calf,' his young voice cracked as he

56

turned to hide from her his quivering lips, 'mooing for its dam, mistook for *la grande passion*. Ah!' he swung round at her again. 'Yes, I, your calf, mistook *au grand sérieux* my need of your udders. That's coarse, isn't it? Which you and all your kind can better understand than more prettily expressed. I've heard the talk that spews around the name of Mrs Chudleigh, Maid of Honour in all but *honour* . . . I honoured you, yes, and I loved you – how one harps upon that word which in our limited English – how different from the French, Italian and Latin tongues, signifies – what? The same word for a child that loves sweets, or a bitch for its master or a whore for her poxed wares, or a demi-rep for the guineas she earns at faro. I know,' he continued loudly, as she covered her ears against this volley of insults hurled at her, yet she could excuse him, seeing him beside himself, 'I know they say you're an adept at the game and gloat on the green baize as a she-ass gloats on thistles.' He clapped hands to his head, rocking to and fro at this horror she had sprung upon him.

And at the suffering she caused him in her vain attempt to shield him from the truth that she was already a wife (God save the mark!) she gave way.

'I have told you lies.' She went to him; she took his hands to her heart. 'Feel how it beats,' she murmured, 'for you. I would give all hope of salvation to be your wife, your own true love . . . but I am bound.'

'Bound?' he gazed at her unbelieving, unsoftened. 'Bound to some whoring leman for this –' he snatched a diamond clasp on the lace of her bodice, tearing it.

'Christ have pity!' she whispered. 'You wrong me who have never wronged you. I cannot marry you but I will give you all that I am, all that you want of me save the right to call me wife.'

But she had only made it worse for him and for herself with this desperate offer.

'To stand in a line – to take my place in turn with those

of whom you've tired or have tired of you?' He was filled with vitriolic loathing of the world that she, by her last abandoned gesture, seemed to represent. 'To father a bastard of yours along with other of your misbegotten brats. "Love?" ' He spat the word at her. ' "My own true love".' She saw on his whitened lips a fleck of spittle. 'Well,' he could now speak jauntily, defiant of her and the façade of what he believed to be her corrupt intent to pacify him, 'I am unbound, released from the bonds of a calf for its cow. Ahah! You choose rightly to call me a calf – calf-headed! You need call me so no more. I've found through you that the last thing you and your world wants is love – despite the Crucifixion!'

And with that he flung out of the room and out of her life for ever.

THREE

So, in order to maintain the secrecy of her abhorred marriage and save for herself and her son the security her position at Court could give, did she sever all hope of happiness with one who she knew would have cherished her as a wife.

Divorce, were it obtainable, was out of the question. Hervey would never allow her the opportunity to be released from him . . . on what grounds? If she were to become the mistress of Hamilton who had so despised her offer attributed by him as a confession that she was just another of those light o' loves misnamed 'Maids of Honour', she would be no nearer obtaining her freedom, for Hervey valued his naval career as highly as she valued her Courtly state; and even should he find her guilty of adultery he would not jeopardize his future, since an officer in His Majesty's Navy must be as Caesar's wife, *sans peur et sans reproche*. Although more than half of the King's naval officers were not without reproach, if without fear in battle, Hervey would not run the risk of a scandal even were he not the guilty party.

The return of Hamilton and Elizabeth's rejection of his renewed proposal of marriage aroused much speculation as why she should remain a spinster. Yet her determination not to take advantage of both wealth and rank stimulated the pursuit of other peers who, until then, had not attempted to consider the much-desired Chudleigh as wife rather than mistress.

Ancaster was the next to try his luck and to offer her his hand and dukedom, with no better result.

To his fellow peers gathered in the gaming room of the

Prince of Wales's country house at Kew, where several tables were arranged for Frederick's cronies to stake their hundreds or thousands of guineas:

'What in hell,' exploded Ancaster, 'is wrong with the Chudleigh that she turns down Hamilton and me?'

'Including myself,' put in Lord Howe, of whom talk had it his advances were not repelled with complete indifference; some even believed that he had been accorded the ultimate favour of this 'Maid of Honour'.

'You too!' exclaimed Ancaster. 'We all thought you'd stormed the citadel.'

'It is too carefully guarded,' Howe ruefully replied.

'Which causes one to ask if her attraction is to women rather than to us?' was Ancaster's retort.

'Unless she were born in the isle of Lesbos,' put in another, disgruntled, having not yet 'stormed the citadel'.

'Chelsea,' said Ancaster, 'where she and I were born.'

'Are you sure?' persisted Howe. 'I've always heard she was born in Devonshire.'

'What matters where?' from the disgruntled Ancaster. 'I wish to God she'd *never* been born to keep us for ever on the hop.'

'Until one of us – if not you, Howe – hops into her bed!'

'Of which,' Howe reluctantly admitted, 'I've never been given the chance more than to see the outside of her bed curtains and when she was *not* in bed.'

'You don't have to see her in bed,' drawled another blade of St James's known as Bubb Doddington, afterwards Lord Melcombe whom Pope satirized as 'Bubo'. His house on the south side of Pall Mall overlooked the Park and was adjacent to the mansion bought by Prince Frederick some ten years before from Lord Carlton, and known as Carlton House. It became derelict under Frederick's son, George the Third, to become the famous pleasance of *his* son, the Prince Regent. That for the future; for the present the company, consisting of several peers of the realm and

60

some lesser fry all considerably in their cups, discussed *ad nauseam* Mistress Elizabeth's refusal of two dukes, a brace of earls and other unsuccessful aspirants, finally to adjudge her if not Sapphic then 'wanting' either mentally or physically.

She still remained supremely indifferent to their various condemnations or suppositions of her virginal state, which were bound to be retailed to her by feline friends. All her spare time she gave to visiting Henry Augustus at Chelsea; and what joy when on one occasion she was proudly shown by his foster-mother, a tiny white seed in his upper empty gum!

'His first tooth!' Elizabeth, adoring, held him to gaze with wonder at this miracle. 'A tooth – and so early!'

'And not a murmur nor complaint, God bless 'im,' said the woman who mothered him for Elizabeth, while she never ceased to regret that she could not yet take him to herself. 'I wonder,' she said anxiously, 'if I should not ask Mr Hawkins to see him? Just to make sure he will suffer no teething trouble. After all, there are many more than this one to come.'

'Yes, madam, t'would be best to call the doctor – just in case he should have any pain when the rest of 'em comes through.'

So Mr Hawkins examined Elizabeth's 'treasure' and pronounced him in perfect health, well advanced for his months and sturdy. 'He'll be a tall boy – look at the length of his legs.'

Elizabeth's only confidante who knew of her marriage other than Mrs Hanmer, Mr Merrill and the third witness Mr Mountenay, was Anne Craddock. She came occasionally to London to visit her mother and would be entertained by Elizabeth at the Conduit Street house. Anne was promised to go with Mrs Hervey to see her son the next time she came to London, but that next time was not to be.

Elizabeth, on leave of absence at Conduit Street, received a message brought by a neighbour of the woman who nursed Henry Augustus, begging Madam to come at once as the baby seemed not so well with his teething.

As fast as a post-chaise could take her Elizabeth hastened to Chelsea, sick with fear while striving to assure herself that the woman could be in a needless fuss, knowing as little about babies and their teething as she herself. . . . All to the good, she kept saying, that the woman should be anxious if he shows signs of pain. All babies suffer when teething and he so advanced Hawkins had said.

The woman met her at the door.

'Not to fret yerself, ma'am. 'Tis only that 'e's not taking his feed so good this last day or two, 'e brings it all up and I thought it best to let you know.'

Elizabeth bent over her son where he lay in his cot. It was springtime dusk, and the light of one candle cast on the ceiling grotesque shadows of the two women. There were little sounds in the darkening room, the faint hiss of logs from the newly lit fire and the fluttering breath of the baby; his wide-open eyes, so vividly blue as if a piece of sky had strayed there, stared up at her whose pale lips framed the words, 'The doctor . . . fetch . . . hurry.'

The woman, pale as herself, hurried while Elizabeth, lifting her son, held him close to her heart so fast and loud beating it seemed he must hear it. Agonized, she saw that those wide unseeing eyes were of a sudden dimmed as though a mist had fallen on them, yet still they stared at her . . . or at infinity?

'Don't!' An anguished cry broke from her. 'Don't stare. O God! . . .' And then a gurgling breath escaped him. She hugged him closer. . . 'It's the wind! Only the wind, my angel. That's all it is.' . . . A spasm shook the tiny body but still those eyes fast dimmed and glazing stared into . . . nothingness.

When the woman came back with the village apothecary who had brought into the world this 'latest addition to the human race', his mother holding him against her frozen heart turned to them saying:

'He has gone with . . . the wind!' And then she fell to laughing a shrill and awful laughter before they could take him from her, who had lost all that made life bearable, all for whom she had lived and loved, and now could love no more.

*   *   *

The catastrophe that had befallen Elizabeth in losing, as she told Anne Craddock, 'the one being in the world who belonged to me and to whom I belonged', wrought in Mistress Chudleigh, as she was to be known for many more years, a noticeable change in her demeanour.

The war between England and her allies against France that temporarily ended in the Treaty of Aix-la-Chapelle was followed by general rejoicing in every excess of orgiastic celebration; in which Elizabeth took part but did not wholly account for her *volte face* from the demure and inaccessible favourite 'Maid' of Princess Augusta to the young, or not now so young, *fille de joie* Chudleigh. She was more than ever in evidence at Vauxhall and other venues in recklessly wanton merry-go-rounds described by that indefatigable tattler, Horace Walpole, with his usual scratches at those on whom it amused him to sharpen his pen.

From him we learn that: 'The gardens at Vauxhall strike the eye prodigiously . . . kept in strictest order and when they are lighted, the sound of music ravishing the ear added to the great resort of company so well dressed and walking about would make one believe he was in the Elysian Fields . . .' Not Horace at his best, but it served its purpose ultimately to resound upon the fortunes, or misfortunes, of Elizabeth Chudleigh. For we have it from Horace that at Vauxhall, Evelyn Pierrepoint, Duke of

Kingston and nephew of Lady Mary Wortley Montagu, first 'cast amorous eyes upon Miss Chudleigh . . .' This Duke, whom Horace tells us with his customary adulation for the peerage, 'was a weak man of the greatest beauty and finest person in England'.

Weak he certainly proved himself in the flexible hands of Miss Chudleigh, still in bondage by her marriage vows. Yet her reason for plunging into the whirligig of fashion that imbibed life to the full was not only on account of the celebrations for the temporary ending of war with France, and her endeavour to readjust her sorrow-laden present in the loss of her child. Hervey, whose duties in active service were suspended with this spurious peace, was back again in London. A letter delivered at Leicester House where, as formerly, he would hang about the gates to waylay her driving past him with no acknowledgement of his presence, again demanded a renewal of his marital rights or else, a repetitive threat, he would expose their secret to Her Royal Highness!

This time Elizabeth felt sure he would keep his word unless . . . But how to prevent it? She must forestall him.

She did. Begging an interview from the Princess on a matter of utmost urgency, she was admitted to Augusta's private sanctum, to which only her favourite 'Miss Chudleigh' was permitted entrance on any matter whether urgent or not.

'Vat den is it, my dear, dat iss so important for you to tell me?'

'Madam,' it needed all Elizabeth's courage to pour out the whole of her pitiful story and the crux of it, the birth and . . . 'Oh, madam,' she fell on her knees. Tears poured from her eyes as she told of her tragic loss, nor did she spare Augusta's shocked ears the horrors of her wedding night and the ultimate enforced consummation of her marriage.

The Princess, touched to the core of her sentimental

heart, joined her own tears to those of the desolate mother. She was raised, embraced. 'My poor child' (no child at twenty-seven but she could have passed for almost ten years younger), 'you haf been most cruelly wrongkt and have suffered enough from zat wrongk. But vy did you not tell me zat before? Did you t'ink I would have sent you away from me? Pah! Zese Englisher rules zat do make zat a Maid of Honour must stay for ever unvedded. Zat is not so in my Faderlandt.'

'Then, your Royal Highness, am I forgiven?'

'Not to forgif – for I am so sad for you zere is not'ink I would not do to help you keep your secret and if so be your husbandt should kom to me mit his tales he would not be receivedt endt you may tell him you haf my assurance zat if he molest you his Admiral vill hear of all zat you haf tell to me.'

The relief from the burden which had weighed so heavily upon her brought forth another gush of tears. More than ever did Elizabeth vow always to be a loyal servant to her mistress, in the exultation that Hervey had no power to deprive her of her position at Court nor claim his lawful and abominable 'rights'.

She lost no time in letting him know of her success in circumventing his intent to ruin her prospects.

The very next day when she drove in her carriage to Conduit Street, he as usual having ascertained when she was given leave of absence from attendance on the Princess, was waiting for her to pass. She called the coachman to halt.

Leaning from the open window she beckoned him. He came to her eagerly, thinking that his latest menace had at last achieved his purpose.

'So! You have thought better than to thwart me. May I drive with you?'

'No! Nor will you ever again *drive* me to distraction with your vile threats. The Princess knows all, and should you dare to approach her you will be dismissed from the

Navy. Your conduct will be reported to the Admiralty. I have Her Royal Highness's assurance of this. You are too late, Hervey. Too late! I have done with you for ever ... Drive on!' to her coachman, regardless that the footman who had climbed down from his box to open the door to admit, as he thought, the officer, for he was wearing his gold-braided uniform. And off she drove, leaving him standing there, biting a hole in the finger of his glove in a fury of frustration.

'You think,' he shouted after her unheard, 'that you have done with me but I've not done with you!'

*   *   *

It was to be an eventful year not only for Elizabeth but for the citizens of London and the courtiers of the King and Prince of Wales.

Relieved of Hervey and his odious presence, for he had ceased now to haunt her, she felt free to indulge in the peace celebrations that went on from the date of the Treaty of Aix-la-Chapelle in October 1748 until the following May, culminating in an extravagant masquerade at Somerset House.

On this occasion 'Miss Chudleigh', as she still continued to be known with full consent of the Princess, caused a furore, not easily forgotten and by many remembered as a notorious scandal with every attempt to damage her name, and bring her down from the pinnacle on which she stood in highest favour with Her Royal Highness and indeed the King himself.

That both the monarch and his son evinced the greatest admiration for 'Miss Chudleigh' but with no apparent response more than was respectfully due to royal patronage, had been a never-ending source of envy from other Maids not so honoured. But Elizabeth, for whom the healing of time in the past year had dimmed the first sorrow of her grievous loss – this she would never forget; yet at

least by tasting the fruits offered in the doubtful enjoyment presented in a labyrinthine pageantry of pleasure,
she could afford to defy whatever was considered or
accepted as the conventions.

The summit of her equivocal achievements to hoist with
her own petard the attempts of her less successful com-
petitors to bring her down who had been so triumphantly
set up, was her appearance at the masquerade dressed or,
more correctly, undressed as Iphigenia.

Her costume, if such it could be called or, as Walpole,
never at a loss to have a dig at her who used to tease him
about his questionable parentage when both were children
at Chelsea, describes it: 'She was so naked you could have
taken her for Andromeda. . . .'

While her sister Maids professed to be shocked and the
gossips enchanted, it seemed her nakedness, if more
closely observed which some of the men dared to do,
revealed her nudity to be no more than a silk skin cover-
ing with a realistic last touch, a circle of fig leaves.

But instead of Perseus arriving from the conquest of the
Gorgons for the rescue of the naked Andromeda, it was
none other than the King whom our ubiquitous tittle-
tattler gives it in one of his numerous letters: 'Our gracious
Sovereign has a mind to believe himself in love, so much in
love that he gave her five and forty guineas. . . .' Whether
charmed by her Andromedan appearance as Iphigenia or
her wit when the Gracious Sovereign gracelessly desired
to place his hand on her breast, 'Your Majesty,' said she,
modestly casting down her eyes, 'I can put it to a still
softer place.' And she laid her hand on the pop-eyed
expectant monarch's forehead.

This, not according to Horace, although it might well
have been, but to another piquant recorder of the Courts
at St James's and Leicester House . . . However that may
be and none present who saw 'Miss Chudleigh' dressed
either as Andromeda, Eve, or Iphigenia, were in slightest
doubt that 'The Gracious Sovereign' had been greatly

67

taken with her. Not so well pleased was his daughter-in-law at the audacious daring of her favourite Maid since, after a gentle rebuke whispered into Miss Chudleigh's unembarrassed ear, she hastily covered her with her veil.

No sooner had the stir caused by the treaty celebrations and by Miss Chudleigh's startling appearance at the masquerade died down, than the frivolous gaieties and dissipations of the two rival Courts were suddenly brought to a halt by an event that affected the whole of London : the earthquake which was spoken of for years as the Wrath of God.

Although such upheavals were not unknown in tropical countries and also reported from parts of central Europe, that England should suffer this violent visitation gave endless opportunity for pietistic Evangelists and tub-thumping Methodists to proclaim at street corners that the Almighty's disapproval of the sins of His people had descended upon them with prophecies of worse to come : the end of a dissolute world.

Smollett, who happened to be in London at the time of the first of these seismic cataclysms, tells that : 'The shock was preceded by a succession of lightning flashes and a rumbling noise as of a heavy carriage over a hollow pavement . . .' too mild a description of the thunderous sounds that rocked the houses and sent terrified citizens rushing into the streets while chimney stacks fell and roofs collapsed. A soldier, driven out of what wits he possessed from listening to the preachings of those who called down upon the heads of sinners the awful damnation that threatened them, ran around crying that a more dreadful fate awaited him and all of his fellows when the second earthquake was about to come as punishment for their wickedness.

A second earthquake did come on the not inappropriate day of April the first, that caused a vast number of the more credulous to flee from the doomed city.

We may presume that Elizabeth, in her dutiful attend-

68

ance on the frightened Princess, was always at hand to offer soothing calm to her mistress, no less than to the King who, equally scared, made valorous attempts not to let anyone see it. But he who had distinguished himself conspicuously at Oudenarde under Marlburian leadership and at Dettingen and had consistently defied his father, the late King, could not defy what he believed to be the Almighty's judgement on him and on his subjects.

Elizabeth's courage, never wanting in disaster whether sent by Heaven or Hell, so impressed the already enamoured King that when all was over and the Wrath of God subsided, Walpole gives us piquant account of the Monarch's latest infatuation: 'The gallant Orantades strode up to Miss Chudleigh and told her he was so glad to have the opportunity of obeying her commands' (presumably her efficiency in dealing with the terror of the earthquake's effect on his son's wife, on the Court and – let us not suggest it – on himself), 'that he appointed her mother housekeeper at Windsor Castle and hoped she would not think a kiss too great a reward . . .' (For what? For services rendered to him or the Princess?) 'He has had a hankering these two years,' continues the irrepressible Horace, 'and why should not a charming face on her side and near on seventy on his produce a title?'

Whether or not her charming face produced a title, it certainly obtained for her mother an appointment that brought Mrs Chudleigh an income of £800 a year, and so relieved Elizabeth of looking after her mother's finances as well as her own.

When the effect of the earthquake and fear of damnation had passed, they who believed themselves judged, and had fled from the city, returned. Once more the Courts enjoyed to their fullest the glitter and sparkle, the jigging and smirking of Vanity Fair, as Thackeray gives it. Once more we see our little George strutting after Elizabeth Chudleigh and ogling the girls, and Lord (John) Hervey, with his painted withered face and on his last spindly legs expectant of an earldom from his dying brother who was not yet to die: and here we have another Duke, Evelyn Pierrejoint of Kingston side-glassing Mistress Chudleigh in the midnight frolics at Vauxhall.

And in the midst of this renewed resumption of the Courts' caperings and junketings, the frolics and the fun, the masquerades and mummery, the scandals and the sneers were brought to a sudden finale, not much to be deplored.

Prince Frederick of Wales, playing tennis, took a blow on the head from a hard ball. A day or two later he was taken with a pleurisy, ordered to bed but disobeying the Court physician he got up and out of it to attend the House of Lords. That he cared nothing for politics nor his royal part in them did not much matter; he liked to be seen in his ermine and scarlet and went back to Carlton House, hot and sweating. Unrobed and dressed in too light a suit, he was driven to Kew where he walked in his gardens and returned to Carlton House.

He had a relapse of his pleurisy, was over it a second time and up and playing cards when seized with a violent fit of coughing.

Caesar Hawkins and another of the Court physicians, Dr Wilmot, were both of the opinion that all was not too well with him, Hawkins being the more pessimistic.

'I don't like it at all,' he told his colleague who had reassured His Royal Highness that he would recover from his cough within a quarter of an hour. He was got to his bed again but the cough continued to rack him. The page in attendance who felt him cold and shaking in every limb called out: 'He's going!'

And he went.

The Princess, having retired to her room, snatched a candle and ran to his bedside, but before she reached him he was gone.

His father, although he had made inquiries throughout

his illness and upbraided him for a fool to go out with a fever on him, believed his attack could not be serious. When he heard the Prince was well enough to attend the House of Lords, 'I told you,' he said to Lady Yarmouth, another of His Majesty's inamorata, 'that he would get over it. He's strong as a horse.'

The King was at cards when a page from Leicester House arrived with the news that the heir to the Throne was no more.

'So!' The King, who had never shown more affection for his son than his son for him, unemotionally remarked to the company in general and to Lady Yarmouth in particular:

'*Fritz ist tode.*'

So that was that, and a solemn-faced boy with a receding chin and the Hanoverian gooseberry eyes mingled tears from his kind little heart to comfort his sobbing mother.

He, the new heir to the Throne, had received no attention from his father's entourage for he had been looked upon as a nonentity, loved by none but his mother and kept more or less in ignorance that he was second in succession to a kingdom.

He was a religious little boy, fond of music and hymn singing, and a great lover of the country at Kew where he had his own garden which he tended and planted with vegetables as well as flowers. He is supposed to have said that when he grew up he would like to be a farmer and have his own farm.

Of course Horace jibed at what he called the 'funeral dirges' and repeated them with relish. The most popular among the many who resented the Hanoverians' succession to the Stuarts was:

> Here lies Fred
> Who was alive and is dead
> Had it been his father I had much rather

Had it been his brother
Still better than another
...Had it been a whole generation
Still better for the nation
But since 'tis only Fred
There's no more to be said.

There was, however, a good deal more to be said with
the reorganizing of 'Fred's' Court at Leicester House that
brought Elizabeth, again appointed Maid of Honour in
attendance on the Princess, who divided her establish-
ments between Leicester House now bereft of its former
frolics, intrigues, and jostling for Princely favours, and
the apartments at St James's set aside for Prince George
and his two brothers.

The new heir to the Throne attracted as little attention
as before, more than to be created Prince of Wales; and
life at the Court of his grandfather, the King, went on as
ever with the goggle-eyed, widowed Defender of the
Faith strutting from one favourite to another. But he kept
the promise made to his charming and devoted wife on
her death bed that he would never marry again. '*J'aurai
des maîtresses.*'

The only one who would never be his '*maîtresse*' no
matter that he, Sultan of his harem, had singled her out
for his especial favour, found her star for a while eclipsed
by the arrival of two new luminaries in her galaxy.

These, the Gunning sisters, come from Ireland with no
fortune but their faces, were described by Walpole to be
'So handsome and both such perfect figures is their chief
excellence, for singly,' added with typical spite, 'I have
seen handsomer women than either.' He was bound to
have a scratch at the lovely pair who had cold-shouldered
this imperishable scribe, having no title and no prospects
more than those from a younger son. They were each
determined, as Elizabeth had been, eventually to secure if
not a duke the next in rank to one.

The Gunnings soon became the toast of the Court gallants who before these two had been seen or heard of were at the feet of 'the Chudleigh'. The sisters lost no time in capturing their prey, of which the younger, another Elizabeth, was sought and won by – the Duke of Hamilton!

'The inconsolable is easily consoled,' chuckled the sparks of St James's, for all knew 'the Chudleigh' had refused him. . . . Too easily consoled for our Elizabeth to take it dispassionately, who although she had been forced to reject this very dukedom, could not but resent that he, having vowed eternal love, had flung out of her life for ever, as he swore at the time she refused him; but she had always believed he would return. Yet here again, ironically, was a secret marriage. This younger Elizabeth would allow no loophole for her capture to escape and inveigled him into a clandestine wedding at Keith's chapel in Mayfair at midnight. . . . History repeated.

Hamilton first sighted the lovely young Gunning at a house-warming given by Lord Chesterfield at his new mansion.

'The Duke playing faro,' again according to Horace, who missed nothing to do with the strawberry leaves (can this be why he built himself a house at Strawberry Hill?) 'saw neither the bank nor his own cards, to lose himself a thousand guineas.'

Two nights afterwards having been fairly caught, and his honourable intentions made and accepted, Hamilton sent for a parson. Having no licence nor ring the clergyman refused to perform the ceremony, ultimately conducted by a less scrupulous Dr Keith, known as the 'Marriage-monger of Mayfair'. A curtain ring was provided to place on the unblushing bride's finger and all went merry as the hushed wedding bells.

The elder Gunning girl soon followed suit with an openly triumphant engagement to Lord Coventry. Although more beautiful than her sister the Duchess,

Maria was more popular because of her naïve malapropisms, a word not then to be found in any dictionary, since the author of *The Rivals* was still in his nursery.

These two, having created sufficient sensation, flaunted their conquests in Paris while Elizabeth, who was now only in attendance on Princess Augusta when commanded, was privileged to make the best of her spare time. This took her to Tunbridge Wells, second only to Bath as the seat of Fashion. And there at the Wells we find her with a second Duke in tow.

We may remember that Evelyn Pierrepoint, Duke of Kingston, had side-glassed Mistress Chudleigh at Vauxhall, and followed an initial introduction with significant pursuit. Since then he had been seen with her continually, and also at Windsor whenever Elizabeth visited her mother, now housekeeper at the Castle. Again her latest conquest was in everybody's mouth. Lady Mary Coke, another gossip, in letters to various friends, gives interesting items concerning Miss Chudleigh still a nominal Maid of Honour.

'When she was here' (at Windsor where Lady Mary had a house) 'she happened to be taken ill, and the Duke of Kingston sat up all night with her. . . .'

So, when Miss Chudleigh was at Tunbridge Wells and promenading with other visitors on the Pantiles in their prodigious hoops, their high powdered heads, their paint; the mode ordained that in this mid-eighteenth century, English women followed the fashion set by France of elaborately painting their faces with heavy applications of red and white, presumably to hide the prevalent ravages of smallpox. And 'The Duke of Kingston,' writes Lady Mary, 'is always with her.'

How far 'with her' he had gone even Lady Mary, as inveterate a tattler as Walpole, could not vouchsafe more than the most oblique conjecture. But we learn from another Lady Mary, the Duke's aunt, Lady Mary Wortley Montagu, 'If the Duke of Kingston marries, I pity . . .' The omission of naming her to be pitied could be supplied by the *ton* of Tunbridge Wells and everywhere else since all knew of the Duke's liaison with a certain Madame la Touche, the natural daughter of a wealthy Parisian banker. The Duke had fallen so madly in love with her in his earlier youth – he was no youth now at forty odd – that he induced her who likely required no inducing to elope with him to England. But marriage, if such were the Duke's intent, was nipped in the bud by Louis, King of France, since Madame's father had financial influence with his Sovereign, whose mistress, la Pompadour, demanded unlimited largesse.

There were frequent allusions to 'Poor Madame la Touche', in Lady Mary Coke's letters: 'She must suffer extremely.' Her extreme suffering to be attributed to the Duke's marked attentions to the admirable 'Chudleigh'.

Elizabeth, back again in London with Kingston at her heels, may have felt somewhat recompensed for the marriage of her former ducal amoret with a younger and more attractive substitute, for here was another and even more eligible Duke of reputedly enormous wealth, not only at her heels but at her feet.

When paying one of her dutiful visits to her mother at Windsor, 'You are getting yourself talked about again', remarked Mrs Chudleigh from behind the tea urn.

'Which is better than never being talked about at all,' replied Elizabeth, with ever so little a smirk. 'And what is the talk about me this time? . . . Please, another cup of this delicious chaney tay.'

Delicious 'chaney tay' supplied – Mrs Chudleigh was never now obliged to 'accommodate' a guest nor to economize in 'tay' at sixteen shillings a pound, told her sharply, 'This time as other times you are coupled with a duke.'

'Not,' put in Elizabeth, the smirk a trifle wider, 'coupled yet. My virginity is still intact.' Her mother had been kept in ignorance of that untimely wedding at

Lainston House for fear lest her knowledge should be spread to all and sundry.

'Then,' said Mrs Chudleigh and bit into a rather stale macaroon to dislodge her porcelain teeth – 'drat the thing, 'tis a misfit. . . . I was about to say if you are still a virgin, which is hard to believe if all accounts of the shocking goings on at Court are true, then you're the exception to prove the rule.'

Elizabeth, holding her handleless cup, 'Quite the exception,' she agreed.

'I hear the Princess, now Dowager Princess of Wales, is far less – one might say retiring – than when the Prince was alive. I can only repeat what I hear.'

'From Lady Mary Coke? An unfailing source of information.'

And her mother, bridling, supplemented: 'Her ladyship and others are constant visitors to me in my official capacity here at the Castle. I therefore hear news of the Court, especially when in residence at Windsor. The Princess has found much comfort in her bereavement from the advice of Lord Bute.'

'Yes, *chacune à son But*,' said Elizabeth demurely.

'Which also,' her mother refilled her own cup, 'was retailed to me that you had the bad taste to tell the Princess.'

'Lady Mary's ears are as long as an ass's and her tongue full of venom as an adder's or Walpole's. As for your official capacity here in the Castle, don't forget,' she reminded her mother, 'that you owe your position to me.'

'At no cost to your virtue, we hope,' Mrs Chudleigh unhopefully added. 'And if the Duke of Kingston's attentions – he is after you, they say – are serious you'd be out of your mind to refuse him as you have refused two other Dukes. You surely don't think to remain for the rest of your life at the beck and call of the Princess who, when the King dies – he can't live much longer – will mean nothing to you or to anyone else.'

76

This thought had indeed been in and not out of Elizabeth's mind; more than ever she regretted her bondage to Hervey. For she felt sure she could yet be the wife of a Duke. But if not – then his recognized mistress.

Whether her mother's advice were regarded, for Elizabeth declined always to take any advice but her own, it is certain talk soon went about that Miss Chudleigh was purchasing land. . . . 'With whose money?' came the inevitable question.

Not *her* money for sure, as her dear 'friends' would have it. Her salary as Maid of Honour would never run to land in Middlesex bought from Lord Berkeley and known to this day as Berkeley Square. She had built herself a house in Hill Street on part of his lordship's estate, and her income of £600 a year scarcely sufficed to keep her in the extravagant style she demanded. And as year succeeded year she acquired more and more property, but conjecture as to the source of her purchases was no longer food for gossip-mongers. They had higher game to stalk than the Chudleigh's friendship with another Duke which was generally assumed to be a permanent *affaire*, and as such accepted as a matter of course where women, whether wives or not, disdained as bourgeois sentiment the chastity of marriage. That the Duke remained unmarried was thought to be her choice, not his; for the fact she was already a wife had leaked out to be licked up by the tongues of those who delighted to taste spicy tit-bits. But *whose* wife – if wife at all – none had been able to discover.

Meanwhile, attention was turned to the hitherto retiring Princess whose husband, the deceased 'Fred', had no more use for her than in her bed as he had used his many extra-marital attractions.

A great change had occurred in the Princess Augusta who mourned the departed for the few months that followed his death. She, being pregnant with a posthumous child, had again fulfilled her wifely duties, having already

77

produced eight children of which this 'latest addition to the Human race' was a daughter, Caroline Matilda.

Although Frederick's toadies alleged him to be 'an exemplary husband' he had earned that much to his credit simply because he was the indubitable parent of his wife's eight children born to him in their fifteen years of marriage and of the daughter Caroline Matilda whom he never lived to see.

That she was his daughter must have caused some disappointment to the scavengers of scandal now directed to the Dowager Princess of Wales.

A figure of some importance destined to play his part in the early life of the future King, no less than in that of the future King's mother, was John Stuart, Earl of Bute.

He had married in 1736 Anne, daughter of Lady Mary Wortley Montagu, who having brought her up never to have a will of her own but strictly to obey parental discipline caused Nemesis to descend upon the exigeant Lady Mary when Anne eloped with John Stuart Bute, as had her mother before her with Anne's father, Wortley Montagu; another marriage in haste to repent at leisure. Not that Anne Bute had ever repented her hasty marriage, for John had never been anything but the most devoted of husbands until . . .

We may, however, assume that Anne discredited the scurrilous rumours which linked her adored John's name with the widowed Dowager Princess of Wales. It was known the defunct heir to the Throne had a great liking for this Scottish Earl and found him to be a gentleman of parts and fascinating manners, very different from the shy awkward youth of twenty years before who had courted the equally shy daughter of the indomitable Lady Mary.

The eldest son of the Dowager Princess of Wales, now a boy of twelve, might any day be King in view of his grandfather's dissolute life, for not even in his seventies did this second George abandon his lively orgies at Herrenhausen, home of his fathers. What more natural, therefore, that the widowed Dowager should turn for advice if not for consolation to Lord Bute? Of him the Princess sought opinion in the training and education of her good little, hymn-singing, quiet – too quiet? – young son. Was his very quietude a good or a bad sign? He was not as other boys, his own brothers, for instance, rowdy, noisy, boisterous in play, but never George. He did not care to play, except on the harpsichord. Excellent, no doubt, that he should show an aptitude for music, but better should he have shown more aptitude for study. His tutors did not think him sufficiently advanced for his age. 'His education,' complained his mother to the sympathetic Bute, 'does gif me to worry. Is he too backvard at his lessons? He seems to care for not'ink but his garten at Kew and wants to be a farmer. . . .' Reassurance from the comforter, guide and counsellor of the future King was always welcome to the widowed mother, as was also his lordship's admittance to her private apartments at Leicester House. The Pages of the Backstairs were ordered to let Her Royal Highness know whenever Lord Bute had arrived.

Long and frequent were the hours spent in this intimate seclusion, while the Princess endeavoured to imbibe from the sympathetic Bute the necessary guidance for the upbringing of the future King.

These almost daily sessions with the Dowager and the graciously attentive Scottish Earl who, instead of returning to his wife and his island of Bute, remained to console the royal widow, to advise her on the welfare of the Prince, caused the worst possible construction to be put upon these visits. Everyone suspected Bute's assiduous attention to the Princess who, at thirty-eight could, if offered, enjoy for the first time in her life the erotic delights of a lover . . . Of course, Walpole declared himself 'convinced of amorous relations between the two as if he had seen them together'.

Elizabeth, always loyal to the Princess, indignantly

repudiated such malicious interpretation of an innocent and wholly understandable reliance on Lord Bute.

'It is cruel,' the Princess tearfully confided to her favourite 'Maid', 'dat dey shuldt say sooch vicked t'ings of me. I haf no one to help me bringk up my son who vill von day be King.'

It was not entirely Elizabeth's friendship for and loyalty to her Royal Mistress that prompted her to defend the Princess, as she needed all the influence from the Throne, or as near to the Throne as the heir's mother could give, to silence the tongues that strove continuously, even while they spat their venom at the Princess, to spit at her.

What if Kingston should hear that she was another man's wife? He had repeatedly offered her marriage, had showered his wealth, his jewels, and adoration upon her with all his persuasive powers to induce her to be his Duchess, as had two other Dukes before him.

But she determined to reject no longer. Marriage being out of the question she would at least accept the next best thing to a legal consummation of Kingston's persistence. She would be his mistress, acknowledged by the world and accepted without prejudice from the Dowager Princess of Wales.

So now the world, or rather that world bounded by St James's and Leicester House where the Prince of Wales and his brothers held their own little Courts, knew of the association between the Duke of Kingston and 'the Chudleigh'.

'How long will it last?' went the envious talk of other Maids of Honour not fortunate enough to have secured so wealthy and ennobled a protector. Little did they, and perhaps 'the Chudleigh', guess it would last to the end of Kingston's life.

FOUR

So for the next few years Elizabeth's association with the Duke came to be accepted as a matter of course. That she still adhered to her spinsterhood ceased to be a matter of discussion or surprise since it was known she would never renounce her appointment with the Princess who for so many years she had so loyally served. It was, however, assumed that the lady considered it necessary to be circumspect in her conduct. There must never be a repetition of her behaviour when she appeared at a masquerade half, if not entirely, naked as Iphigenia.

That episode had been more or less forgotten. There were matters of more moment to discuss than 'the Chudleigh' who had sent two Dukes packing. And why? ... Never mind. She had captured Kingston and obviously made good use of his wealth if not of his title.

While the circle of frivolity, dancing, gaming, unceasingly revolved, Elizabeth, adept at cards, continued regularly to frequent the King's green baize. As for that old rip, he continued to languish after 'the Chudleigh', yet got no farther in his pursuit than to lead her in the minuet that was the then fashionable craze of ball-rooms.

But in the midst of the aged pagan's visit to Herrenhausen where he divided his leisure months between his beloved Hanover and the Britain over which he indifferently reigned, all eyes, or at least those eyes not bleared and seared from late-night gallantries and other dissipations, were turned to 'that serious-minded little boy' of whom it was said: 'He is strictly honest but wants frank and open behaviour that makes honesty appear amiable.' Precisely what was meant by that ambiguous

description of the heir to the Throne by Lord Waldegrave, one of his tutors and not the most wisely
chosen since at the age of eleven the Prince of Wales
could scarcely read English, is not certain although he
was the first of the Hanoverian kings to be born in
England. Yet unlike his father and grandfather he was
such a 'good honest little boy', that as he neared manhood
he would brood upon the profligacy of his grandfather's
Court. His mother would often suggest to her 'good Lord
Bute' that 'The Prince is too attentive to the sins of his
neighbours'.

Who exactly were his neighbours we do not know, nor
most probably did his mother, for he was always retiring
and aloof. Even before the death of his father he had few
friends of his own age, and the only one of his brothers
for whom he seemed to have any affection was Edward,
Duke of York. As for girls, his mother must have been
relieved to see that, unlike Edward, he showed no interest
in her Maids of Honour, nor they in him.

'He is not like ze oder boys of his age,' the Princess
complained to her 'goot Lord Bute' upon whom George
also relied as guide, philosopher and friend; his 'dearest
friend' as he was soon to regard him. And one other, not
a man, a woman; who else but his mother's favourite
Maid of Honour, Mistress Chudleigh?

She first attracted the Prince's attention when he was
about fourteen, and this attraction increased as the months
of his monotonous, detached young life crawled by. . . .
Crawled, because young George's life was never destined
to race to its end as did the lives of his forbears race along
their downward years. The wintered ashes of their
memories are scattered on a palimpsest as 'grossly adulterous, sensual, licentious, godless' – every exaggerated
threnody that could be hymned to them, but never to the
third of these Georges. The friendship, or indeed affection,
of George, Prince of Wales, for Miss Chudleigh is of
importance, less to the life of Britain's future King than to

the life of Elizabeth, for she is said to have aided and abetted the young heir to his grandfather's Throne in his youthful infatuation for a pretty Quakeress several years older than himself. She was one Hannah Lightfoot, a linen draper's daughter with whom George fell violently in love.

So far as Elizabeth is concerned in the Prince's first adolescent love affair, it seems she often accompanied him on his walks from Leicester House to St James's Palace, for he preferred her attendance to that of his tutors or Lord Waldegrave. Elizabeth liked the boy and was thankful for his mother's sake that George showed no signs, as yet, of having visited upon him the sins of his fathers.

We are told that the then fifteen-year-old Prince sighted the pretty young Quakeress in the window of her father's linen shop at the corner of St James's market, and that he asked Miss Chudleigh the name of this young lady, which Elizabeth would have made it her business to know and also to keep an eye on the 'good little' George who seemed to be too interested in the delectable Hannah.

That this Miss Lightfoot belonged to the Society of Friends must have made her more desirable to the 'godly' George, whom his grandfather deplored for reading the Bible and singing hymns instead of enjoying the comically ribald ditties of the day in which the old King and his Court delighted.

From his first glimpse of Hannah in her demure grey gown, her white cap that did not entirely conceal stray locks of bright gold hair, George's interest in her became apparent, much to Elizabeth's unease. She soon realized there were clandestine meetings when the Prince, evading vigilance from her and his tutors, would sneak out to see Hannah at closer quarters than through the barred windows of Friend Lightfoot's shop where his daughter would display her father's linen wares to passers-by. There would have been, Elizabeth surmised, no discouragement on the part of the quakerish Hannah who, full of pretty palpitations and an eye to the main chance, was immensely flattered by and did not discourage the pursuit of the Prince of Wales. That she could ever be his wife she knew would be impossible, although we are asked to believe he had entreated her to marry him in secret. This, of course, is pure apocrypha but it is fairly certain that George was sufficiently enamoured to have it in mind to marry her when he should be of age. And this is where Elizabeth comes into the story, unearthed more than half a century later, in an issue of the *Monthly Magazine* of 1815.

Elizabeth felt herself in part responsible for having on several occasions walked with the Prince by the linen draper's shop even after she had observed the Prince's interest in linen sufficiently to stare at the goods handled by Hannah with an exchange of sheepish eyes from him, and the blinking of remarkably long eyelashes lowered on the blushful cheeks of the young person who engaged his amorous attention – and, good heavens – his intention!

Knowing as Elizabeth knew to her cost where love's first sight could lead, she wisely informed the Dowager Princess of the Prince's unfortunate attachment.

Whereupon, having heard with dismay all that her favourite Maid had to tell, the Princess fell into the vapours. Hysterically she informed Miss Chudleigh to find a husband – 'any husbandt – the sveep, the dustman – any-von to marry dis creature who has bevitched ze Prince – so yong a boy, so goot and so innocent. Never does he t'ink of ze girls. Ze King he make fun of George because he reads ze Bible and say his prayers. Endt now, O my dear Elizbet' . . . The Princess must have been in a rare taking to call her 'goot Miss Chudleigh' by her Christian name, which she seldom used since she had wept on her Maid's shoulder at the death-bed of her husband, whose departure from his ill-spent life had been mourned by none save his wife and she only for three or four months . . .

84

'*Gott im Himmel*! Vat,' sobbed the Dowager, 'are ve to do? Is it true zat ze Prince vill marry her?'

'Not only marry her, Madam, but abduct her – persuade her at *her* instigation I have no doubt – into a secret marriage.'

'As you shouldt know all about zat to your sorrow,' moaned the Princess, 'my poor Elizabet'. . . . *O, du lieber Gott, quelle horreur terrible!* Vat misery haf come upon me?'

'Have no fear, Your Royal Highness,' Elizabeth as ever soothed and comforted, 'I will see that the Prince is rescued from this designing young person's coils. Leave all to me.'

All was left to her. Having taken alarm Elizabeth took advice from a reliable source of whom we have no intimation as to his name or how he came to be involved in rescuing the Prince from that young person's coils, other than given by the correspondent of the *Monthly Magazine*. But we know that neither sweep nor dustman was found to marry the enamoured Prince's Quakeress, whose seeming piety and godly devotions must have gone a long way to induce the equally pious and godly Prince into contemplating taking her to wife as his future Queen Consort . . . *Gott im Himmel* indeed!

One circumstance about the whole deplorable affair is that Elizabeth procured an intermediary well paid by George's mother, for we may be sure Elizabeth would not have called upon her Duke however willing he would have been to hand her over X hundred pounds without asking why she needed it. This unnamed agent managed to provide for Miss Lightfoot a husband, one Isaac Oxford, assistant to Barton, the grocer of Ludgate Hill, much to the relief of Hannah's parents and the elders of The Society of Friends. They who had got wind of the Prince's attentions, whether honourable or not, went in fear lest they be tried for treason and landed in prison as traitors to the Crown and State. Thus was ended this singular contretemps. That

Elizabeth appears to have been involved in the Prince's entanglement with Hannah is all we know of it concerning Miss Chudleigh. But we may believe that the Dowager Princess of Wales was more than ever devoted to her 'goot Elizabet', second only in her warm regard for her 'goot Lord Bute'.

From now on and for many years to come Elizabeth gained complete ascendancy over her Duke and continued to buy houses with resources far beyond her six hundred a year as Maid of Honour to the Dowager Princess of Wales, who could never be grateful enough to her 'Elizabet' for rescuing George from the designing Hannah.

So we learn that Miss Chudleigh took a house in the village of Knightsbridge which was named Ennismore House, afterwards to be renamed Kingston House, on the site of which, more than two hundred years later, rose a luxury block of flats.

That Kingston was for ever urging Elizabeth to be his wife became known to everyone connected with the Court; and that 'the Chudleigh' still remained a spinster ceased to be the talk of the Town. Her marriage to Hervey also became known, or guessed, to a good many, but Elizabeth was never troubled by him who kept out of her way for reasons of his own. He was not at all anxious to take her as wife any more than she would have taken him as husband when she had every advantage of wifehood except in name with the wealthy and adoring Duke of Kingston. He too, must have guessed why she refused to marry him. Yet she might not be content to remain for ever under his protection even though he gave her all as his mistress other than his name to which, as his wife, she would have been entitled.

Walpole, as usual, scribbling round to his intimates, records that her relationship with the Duke – Horace, of course, knew all about that – was no bar to her status at Court. However, she preferred to live in seclusion when not attendant on the Princess. She took a house at Finchley where the Duke could visit her unmolested by importunate callers. She enjoyed her garden full of fruit and flowers and on her vacations she and the Duke lived in happy domesticated quiet; he, pottering about the garden with her, and she no longer requiring the frivolities of life at Court to relieve her mind as to whether Hervey would turn up again to claim her. So the years passed contentedly while she occupied herself with the lavish furnishings of Ennismore House, described as 'quite out of London', being situated east of another village, Kensington, where the one street was badly lighted, a favoured haunt of 'gentlemen of the road', as highwaymen were called, and footpads; and on the village green at Knightsbridge stood a maypole around which Elizabeth would often see the girls and boys dancing and singing on May Day.

Thus did she enjoy the only happiness she had known in all her chequered life until . . .

It must be remembered when at the time of her marriage with Hervey she had no notion he would ever stand a chance of succeeding to the earldom of Bristol. But since that secret wedding some fifteen years earlier, the immediate successors to the earldom had died; not only Hervey's father and two of his sons, but a third of them, now the immediate holder of the earldom, had no children, and Hervey, her abhorred and lawful husband, was his heir.

Although the Duke would have married her the moment she was free of Hervey, and notwithstanding that she really did love her Duke who so adoringly loved her, he was neither young nor in good health. Never licentious he had, none the less, spent a hot-headed youth and now past middle-age was reaping the ill-effects of too much wine and women. He had settled down in peace with his Elizabeth but she feared she would certainly outlive him. And although she would be well provided in the event of his death, she could not expect as his mistress an income to be anywhere near that which she would have had as

87

his wife. But as Countess of Bristol she would be a peeress, and a title meant more to Elizabeth than even the wealth and devotion of a Duke were she not legally his Duchess.

Yet how to establish her right to be the wife of the Earl of Bristol when Hervey succeeded to the earldom which might be sooner than she dared hope, since his brother was reputed to be not in the best of health? To abandon her Duke would have hurt her almost as dreadfully as it would have hurt him, but she still thought she should make her marriage known as the wife of the heir to an earldom. Yet how to set about proving her claim when Hervey should succeed to the title? After fifteen years of that lamentable marriage performed in the dark little chapel which, even if witnesses were still alive, had produced no register would present some difficulty, although surely proof enough if there *were* witnesses to swear they were present at that secret wedding. But what of the chief witness, the clergyman, Mr Amis? She guessed he must be very old now, he was old when he married her to Hervey and – supposing the present Earl did not die, should outlive his heir and brother, Hervey, she would then be free to marry her Duke. But the chances against Hervey predeceasing his brother were too great a risk. There was only one way out of it. She must go and see her cousin or rather her father's cousin, Mr Merrill. Her Aunt Hanmer – she was still alive but Elizabeth had no wish to consult *her* to verify the marriage. No, it must be Merrill. He had always been friendly, too friendly, the old goat! And he had no hand in the interception of Hamilton's letters. It was that damned old bitch her Aunt Hanmer who had attempted to ruin her life. The fact that she hadn't ruined it, had helped her, although she did not know it, upon her eventful career, decided Elizabeth, as she paced her drawing-room. She must go straight down to Lainston, rake up old Merrill – he would be old now – and ask his advice.

Her 'Evie' (Evelyn Pierrepoint, Duke of Kingston) was

dozing in his study when she went to him after deciding what must be done. Leaning over him she noted with a pang how grey was his hair and thinned without his wig.

'Evie, darling,' she kissed a bald patch on top of his head, 'My Aunt Hanmer – I've told you of my Aunt Hanmer and how she stole the letters that Hamilton, to whom I was betrothed, had written to me and because I didn't answer his –'

'I know all about that,' the Duke woke, yawningly to interrupt. 'Ah-ah-Ah'm thankful she did steal his letters or I should never have had you, my adored one. Well, and what of this aunt?'

'She is ill – I heard this morning – she wants to see me,' rapidly improvised his adored one. 'I expect she is dying and wishes to ask my forgiveness for what she did to me, so I feel I ought to go.'

'I don't see why,' the Duke said sulkily, after what she did to you and Hamilton, although I benefit by it, thank God!'

'Hamilton has been easily consoled. Anyway, I feel it my duty to go to her.'

'Can't your mother go instead of you?'

'No, they were never fond of each other and Mamma can't possibly leave Windsor at such short notice, so I'll have to go.'

And go she did, nor did she stand upon the order of her going more than to promise her 'Evie' she would only be gone for one night.

She travelled by post-chaise to Winchester and put up at the Blue Boar Inn. From there she sent a messenger to Merrill at Lainston House begging him to come and see her on a matter of the utmost urgency. She had determined not to consult with him at his house, where she knew her Aunt was still living as the guest of charity, so did she disdainfully think of 'that old bitch'.

Accordingly Merrill came at her bidding. She had not

seen him nor he her since that fateful 'honeymoon' at Lainston House. Taking her hands in his he gazed at her wonderingly:

'You have not changed. You are still young and handsome as ever.'

'Flatterer!' She could not say the same of him, for he had always been heavy-jowled, bucolic, puffy-eyed as she remembered him when a girl, and to her mind hideous.

But: 'Nor have you changed, Cousin Merrill. You were always good-looking and you still are handsome as you were all those years ago.'

'Come, come.' He snorted with pleasure. She bade him be seated, rang for refreshment – 'a bottle of your favourite – now what was it?'

He prompted her 'Oporto, which I should not drink for it does not agree with my gout.' He spread thick sausage fingers, 'I suffer for my four bottles a day which I have eliminated to – well, barely two.'

Then after some such pleasantries and liberal port and cracknel biscuits, Elizabeth tactfully brought in the subject of her urgent summons to 'Cousin Merrill'.

He heard her out attentively. His shrewd little eyes peering from folds of wrinkled flesh narrowed and widened as she told him:

'I feel I ought to produce evidence of my marriage. I suffered humiliation enough from that hasty wedding, but now – well, Cousin, if Hervey is to be Earl of Bristol I am entitled to be his Countess, even if I refuse to live with him as his wife, for I swore I never would. He behaved with such cruelty to me – I can't go into all that now, but you must have heard from my Aunt Hanmer that I refused to live with him as his wife because I could not remain in attendance on Her Royal Highness if she knew I was married.'

Old Merrill thumbed the first of his three flabby chins.

'So you have lived as a Maid though not a maid ever since?'

She nodded casting up her eyes. 'I love the Princess and she relies on me.'

'You would lose your position at Court if your marriage is known to the Princess?'

'No,' she shook her head, 'my marriage is known to the Princess. I confessed to her and she forgave me, and said she would respect my secret. She could not, she said, have me leave her. I am the only one of all her Maids of Honour whom she cares for and can trust. In fact –' Elizabeth laid it on with a tearful trowel, 'Her Royal Highness has suffered even more than I in her marriage with the late Prince of Wales. More than I because I only endured Hervey for three days and she, poor lady, endured her husband for thirteen years.'

Merrill was suitably impressed.

'You have done very well for yourself, I must say, to be so favoured.'

'I have only done my duty, Cousin.' More casting up of eyes heavenward as if to attract a celestial halo around her shameless head.

The old fool, said she to her inner self, he can't possibly know about Evie and me – or any of the others. 'I have lived as a spinster, Cousin, deliberately that I may continue to serve my Princess, believe me, not for any personal honour but for my love of her. Yet now I have to remind you that if I do seem as young as ever in this favourable candlelight' (for it was a darkening winter's afternoon) 'I am no longer young. I am' – she subtracted some three years – 'thirty-five.'

'Pooh! A mere child compared to my thirty years or more than that. So you wish to be acknowledged as Hervey's wife without having to, er, to cohabit?'

'That is so. I don't see why I should not be legally entitled to be his Countess if he should inherit the earldom of which he is sole heir. You see, Cousin Merrill,' she spoke now in earnest and with determined emphasis, 'I have had to support myself all these years on a bare sufficiency as Maid of Honour and I do feel that my lawful husband should at least give me what is my due as his wife, if I grow too old to earn my livelihood. The Princess does have an age limit to her Maids of Honour, and much as she cares for me that limit could not be abolished and I should be penniless if my lawful husband did not fulfil his obligations to his wife.'

'And,' suggested Merrill with a knowing gleam in those puffy-lidded eyes, 'his Countess.'

'That,' she said smoothly, 'is also a consideration if he lives to inherit his earldom. We are all in God's hands.' Again that lifted look to heaven. 'None of us goes until God will invite us.'

'That is so,' agreed Merrill with the uneasy hope that his invitation from the Almighty might be long delayed. 'So how can I be of assistance to you, my dear?'

'I was wondering if you know whether Mr Amis, the clergyman who performed the marriage service in Lainston chapel, is still alive.'

'That I can assure you, but he has retired now and is living here at Winchester. He would be an important witness, and I too, and your Aunt Hanmer. We all three can substantiate the marriage if called upon to do so.'

A wave of relief overswept her.

'Then could I – we – if you would be so kind as to accompany me to visit him –'

She paused while waiting for his answer which came with equally assuring promptitude.

'But most certainly.' He took out of his breeches' pocket a cumbersome watch. 'It is too late now, but tomorrow? I will call for you at eleven o' the clock. You are conveniently situated here for this inn is almost directly opposite the house of Mr Amis. I often pay him a visit as he is, I regret to say, in poor health. I will inquire now,' he rose, 'if tomorrow and at what hour will be suitable for us to call.'

In a fever of impatience Elizabeth awaited Merrill the

next morning. He had come back from the clergyman's house to inform her Mrs Amis had said her husband was ill in bed but would be well enough to receive Mr Merrill and Mrs Hervey, both of whom he would be pleased to see, in especial Mrs Hervey whom he well remembered having performed her marriage to Mr Hervey.

Merrill had not told the clergyman's wife the nature of their visit. She believed it merely an informal call on Elizabeth's part to see again the clergyman, having heard, while staying at Lainston House, that he was not in the best of health.

Mrs Amis could, of course, have known nothing of Mrs Hervey's association with the Duke of Kingston, or neither she nor her husband might have been so pleased to welcome her. But before Elizabeth and Merrill were conducted to the clergyman's bedroom, Mrs Amis was told of a reason other than the anxiety of Mrs Hervey on behalf of the infirm Mr Amis.

There ensued at the bedside of the aged clergyman a lengthy conversation of which the main issue arose as to whether there had been a certificate – in fact, a registration of her marriage.

There was none; but Merrill in the meantime had provided himself with a stamped paper for which he must have been busy since early morning to have obtained it, to save the feeble old Amis unnecessary trouble. He now produced it for the clergyman to sign.

But the reverend gentleman was in a state of perturbation as to the legality of signing such a certificate without the advice of an attorney, since he confessed he knew little of the law appertaining to the registration of a marriage. This would necessitate delay while a lawyer could be found to draw up the required document at such short notice.

Elizabeth was now greatly put about. What if an attorney could not be found – at once? How much longer to be kept here on tenterhooks and Evie expecting her home tonight! Always intolerant of any thwarting of her desires if amorous or not, and in this case of more concern to her than any romantic purpose, she fretted and fussed regardless of poor old Amis's condition. He, or possibly Merrill, to further Elizabeth's exasperation, raised the question as to the advisability of Mrs Hervey's presence while the document was prepared and finalized.

At last she was persuaded by Merrill that it would be better were she not present at the signing of the document for should Hervey learn of the transaction she would be able to swear ignorance of the whole business. Not quite true but true enough to avoid perjury in a Court of Law should Hervey wish to contest the certificate which, knowing him, she judged would be more than likely were he Earl of Bristol.

Merrill who was most pleasantly involved in all this business, finding it an enjoyable departure from the monotony of his life at Lainston during the winter months when there was hardly any racing in his vicinity, named a Mr Spearing as the most reliable and best-known attorney in Winchester.

Summoned by Merrill, he came to the house during the afternoon; and, on Merrill's suggestion advised that Elizabeth should go back to the inn while the certificate was being drawn up. This she positively refused to do. Merrill, however, would not hear of her being a witness to any of these legal proceedings, so it was finally decided by Elizabeth, and reluctantly agreed by Merrill, that she should hide in a closet adjoining the bedroom, while the attorney and the clergyman were satisfied she had returned to the inn. Not for the first time was she forced to hide in a closet, as she had every reason to remember.

The proceedings went lengthily on while Elizabeth, her ear to the keyhole, knelt to hear as much as she could understand of the lawyer's opinion on the case. She gathered that the man of law ponderously declared this manner of establishing evidence was not the most regular, nor would it have the decisive effect of proving the marriage to have taken place. It could – he went on and on propounding legal and incomprehensible obstacles – while he decided that what he called a 'check book' should be brought, and the marriage registered in the presence of Mrs Hervey. This he maintained was essential.

After more discussion, while Elizabeth endured pins and needles in her cramped position, a book was brought from the lawyer's office by a clerk, and Elizabeth made her appearance, without being discovered eavesdropping at the door, by leaving Mr Amis's house and going downstairs to the front entrance where she rang the bell and was admitted by Mr Merrill, who had sent a message, so he told the lawyer, to bring her over from the inn.

She was introduced as the Honourable Mrs Hervey to this Mr Spearing (and why Honourable she inquired, for his father had received but a courtesy title as the son of an Earl, in which case Hervey as a younger son would have had no title at all). The lawyer then inscribed in a fair clear hand the entry under, Births, Marriages, Deaths:

The 4th August 1744, married the Honourable Augustus Hervey to Miss Elizabeth Chudleigh, daughter of Colonel Thomas Chudleigh deceased, in the Parish Church of Lainston.
                    Signed

                                Thomas Amis

There was some discussion as to whether, in view of the enfeebled health of Mr Amis, the certificate should be handed over to Merrill to hold should evidence be necessary to prove the marriage.

This was agreed, but when Merrill subsequently died, soon after his part in the transaction, the certificate was then given into the keeping of the next incumbent of the parish church at Lainston. He, having made a fair copy of the register with the births, marriages and deaths of that year, returned the original 'check book' to the widow of the Rev. Mr Amis.

This for the future; but all that at present concerned Elizabeth was the written evidence of her marriage to the Hon. Augustus Hervey. She wished she had been aware of this insignificant title to his name, for she would have preferred to have been known as the Honourable Mrs Hervey than plain Mrs, a prefix used for matrons and maids alike. However, all that really mattered was she could now rest assured that any day, month or year she might be the Countess of Bristol.

She could not have foreseen that all these elaborate precautions were unnecessary to secure for herself the right to be a peeress, wife of an Earl, if not the wife of a Duke, which she knew was impossible. For the supposedly dying Earl of Bristol did not die! He lived on for several years, well recovered from what had been thought to be a fatal illness, and his heir, the Honourable Augustus, might never succeed him for, as rumoured, the Earl was seeking a wife and in that case could produce an heir who would not be the man with whom Elizabeth had gone to such pains to prove her hated marriage.

But not gifted with clairvoyance she was satisfied her purpose had apparently been achieved.

Her 'Evie' was waiting her arrival at the house in Finchley and evinced some annoyance that she had been gone for two nights instead of one as she had told him. Her inventive powers at once overcame that difficulty. Her Aunt had insisted she should stay longer at Lainston, and as the doctor attending Mrs Hanmer advised his patient would require her niece to remain until she was out of danger, she perforce had to remain that extra night and day.

She now was busy with her Knightsbridge house, and since she found it tiring to go back and forth from Finchley to superintend the decorations, furnishings and all to do with the purchase of the property, she and her Duke returned to Ennismore House, as the residence at Knights-bridge was known until it later became Kingston House. There were rooms already sufficiently furnished for Eliza-beth and the Duke to occupy, and there they remained with weekly intervals in the country at their Finchley estate.

Once the house and its sumptuous furnishings and interior decorations were completed, Elizabeth gave a great house-warming party to which everyone who was anyone was invited; ostensibly the entertainment being given by the Duke, Elizabeth acting as hostess, but all now knew of the relationship. The party was held for the birthday of Prince Edward, the Duke of York for which he, a lad still in his teens, was guest of honour.

Walpole, of course, had much to tell his numerous correspondents concerning the lavish style in which the Duke expended what must have been a fortune . . . 'There was a concert for Prince Edward's birthday, and at three a vast collation for all the Town.' Presumably 'all the Town' meant all the guests who flocked there as much from curiosity as to be able to say they had met and been presented to the first in succession to the Heir Apparent. 'That serious-minded honest little boy' who if invited, did not come. His mother, although she knew of her favourite Maid's relationship with the Duke, may have thought it not quite in keeping with her George's high position to honour her 'Elizabet's' intimacy with the Duke of King-ston by his appearance at his brother's birthday ball. The Princess would not for the world have the Heir thought to condone even the least irregularity of conduct regarding her 'goot Miss Chudleigh', notwithstanding that the Dow-ager Princess must be eternally grateful to her 'Elizabet' for bringing to an end that appalling episode of the Quakeress which could have been a calamity not for George alone but for the nation.

Walpole, one of the 'Town' who had been invited and

with alacrity accepted, gives his usual denigration of anything to do with 'the Chudleigh' and in this case the house bestowed upon her by the Duke. . . . 'Not fine nor in good taste' (which is typically unfair, for Elizabeth's taste was impeccable), 'loaded with finery', as Horace sneeringly describes it. 'Pictures, chests, cabinets, commodes . . . everything on earth. A glass case full of enamels, lapis lazuli, cameos, toothpick cases, all kinds of trinkets, things that she told me were her playthings, thrown down in every corner. The Virgin Mistress began the ball with the Duke of York' (Horace has a dig at him too), 'dressed in a pale blue tabby which I told him if he danced much would soon be tabby all over. . . .' Horace would never miss a chance to bring in the fact that he had talked with Royalty, which may be taken for as much or little as his volatile pen could tell.

So the festive season rollicked to its end, and the 'Virgin Mistress' of Ennismore House continued to enjoy her intimacy with her 'Evie' now accepted by the *ton*.

The second Hanoverian George had also rollicked to his end – the end of a long road beset with milestones to mark a series of events, none particularly spectacular; and those of his valorous part in the Marlburian wars were not so memorable to him as his love of and perpetual grief for the loss of his wife, the estimable Caroline most revered and respected of all these Georgian Consorts. In his seventy-seventh year and the thirty-fourth of his reign he could still shed tears as he recalled he had never known a woman worthy to buckle his wife's shoe.

On a morning in October of that year, 1760, the King went to his closet, came back to his room and rang for his chocolate as usual. He gulped the hot syrupy liquid, threw it all up, flopped forward on his breakfast tray and died.

On that same morning a boy, just two and twenty, riding from his house at Kew to London, was stopped on his way by a King's Messenger. (His Messenger though he knew it not.) He saw the bowed head of him who stayed the Prince on the King's highway; he saw the black livery hastily donned and kept in readiness for some such sudden occasion.

The sight of that lowered head and the news imparted in a hushed voice gave George instantaneous shock as knowledge dawned to drain the healthy pink from his cheeks, from which he at once recovered to bid his Messenger: 'Say not a word to them,' with a backward jerk of his head to his three attendants. 'I return to Kew – now. My horse is lame. He has picked up a stone. Can you not see how he is lame? You understand?'

The Messenger understood.

No distance back to Kew. He walked his mount, keeping to the fiction of a stone in the horse's hoof, and refusing to ride one of his servant's horses instead.

Theirs not to question the order of their Prince – No! Their King! For each man of them guessed what that funereal black livery and the low-voiced murmur of the King's Messenger had meant to this chubby-faced, rosy-cheeked youth, grandson of an old man lying in state who – God be praised! – was no more. And this lad here, this 'strictly honest, pious, pure Defender of their Faith', born in England as were they and their fathers and grand-fathers before them of good old English stock, was their Sovereign Ruler and their King – God bless him!

His own personal groom who, at first, showed surprise at the Prince's quick return, for he had been gone but half an hour, was told:

'I have said my horse is lame. You are to say nothing to the contrary.'

The groom, head groom of the stables, bowed low.

'Yes, Your . . . yes, Sir, the horse is lame.'

He too had understood but he bowed noticeably lower than when he had bowed the Prince of Wales on his way less than an hour before. The Prince would always visit his stables and look to his horse before mounting him.

He then went to his room and bade his valet change his riding habit for his London suit. He too may have understood why the Prince must go immediately to London although he had been told nothing of that which would soon be known to the whole of Great Britain and Ireland.

On the following day when the Accession to the Throne was proclaimed at Savile House opposite his residence of Leicester House, a vast multitude of London's citizens shouted, yelled one-voiced and whole-heartedly:

'*God Save The King!*'

*   *   *

The Maids of Honour at Leicester House, or Maids of *Dis*honour as known by the younger blades of St James's who had no taste for stale sweets left over from the old King's harem – *they* did not rejoice. Those who had been in high favour when the late King with his red face, his goggly eyes, and white hair – no need for him to wear powder – had strutted from one to the other leering, feeling, fondling, raddled, they of his choice wept, not so much for the loss of him as for all they had lost of his bounty. Gone were the intrigues, the glitter and sparkle and dissipation of the old King's Court. All knew what the Court of this third King George would be; no gaming, no dancing, no frolics, no fun, and no possible chance of bestowment of favours demanded and willingly granted. Hymn singing, Bible readings, dirges and prayers would be the order of this King's day. His morals were inviolate. He could never have had a girl unless it were the Quakeress.

'Not even her,' went the assumption. 'He would have married her had not the Chudleigh nipped that in the bud!' And was rewarded by the constant gratitude and continued favour of the Dowager Princess of Wales. 'As for "the Chudleigh"!' . . . Words failed them as to her who had led the Duke of Kingston by the halter, 'if not to the altar', giggled Mrs Ashe, one of the girls who had her knife in the pretty neck of Elizabeth, although sworn her dearest friend.

She, another Elizabeth, had eloped with Lady Mary Wortley Montagu's scoundrelly son, and lived to regret it and loathed him as much as our Elizabeth regretted and loathed her marriage to Augustus Hervey, if not for the same reason.

Yes, this George would be the end of all the fun and games of the erstwhile Maids of Honour at the Court of the late King. They all wore mourning correctly, Elizabeth also, keeping religiously to traditions due to the death of a monarch, but so soon as she decently could discard funereal trappings, she emerged into colours and a surfeit of new clothes, gowns, furbelows, gewgaws, hats – oh, those hats! We have seen some of them in the early portraits of Gainsborough before the enormous towering 'heads' became the fashion, so high that their faces looked to be in the middle of their bodies.

A little milliner from Cranbourne Alley brought to Elizabeth at Ennismore House, bandboxes full of hats, caps, and all sorts of things for Madam's choice, paid for by the Duke who cast eyes, as noted by Madam, on the pretty little milliner. We shall hear more of her later. She was much patronized by ladies of the *ton*.

Elizabeth was now much in evidence at Court functions. And the as yet uncrowned King sought her advice in a second love affair as he had with his first 'entanglement' with Hannah Lightfoot, well and truly married to her grocer's assistant so we hear no more of her.

What we do hear and which all the Court and the man and woman in the street would hear, was that the King had fallen madly in love for a second time, not with anything so common as a linen draper's daughter, but with Sarah Lennox, daughter of the Duke of Richmond.

George, when Prince of Wales, had first set eyes on her making hay in the grounds of Holland House. Struck with her beauty, extolled by Walpole who with his usual reverence for the nobility, says:

'Her beauty is not easily described!' Whereupon he goes on effusively to describe her as having: 'The finest complexion, and prettiest person ever seen . . . A pretty mouth, remarkably fine teeth, an excess of bloom in her cheeks,' and so on. The excess of adjectives is inexhaustible.

She had lovers enough for the 'excess of her bloom' without the Prince of Wales as her suitor; but a future King was not to be discouraged, although the young lady, she was only sixteen, had a head on her 'prettiest person'.

Elizabeth, in the confidence of the Prince of Wales, noted that when he became King, his interest in the lovely Sarah had waned with the excitement and onerous business to do with his Accession that gave him no time to turn his thoughts to love. But now, while he waited for his Coronation, he renewed his visits to Holland House, and he too was making hay in his courtship while the sun shone on Sarah and on him who asked for no greater joy than to have her consent to be his Queen.

Yet Lord Bute and the King's mother were of no such mind. Bute, always at the elbow of the Dowager Princess, asked His Majesty to consider what he contemplated.

'We know of Kings of England who have married commoners' (he forbore to remind George of a King of England who had married five commoners, other than his first and lawful wife, Catherine of Aragon, from whom, contrary to Popish rule, he obtained a divorce). 'But it would be unwelcome to your subjects, Sir, were you not to follow in the footsteps of your father and grandfathers.'

George again protested firmly. For all his piety and honesty he had an obstinate streak in him that would brook no opposition to a purpose on which he was determined. He told his 'dear friend' as much in careful words and was asked sternly: Did he want to break his mother's heart?

Again George protested, his temper rising – which, in later years, would rage in brainstorms – that his Crown did not outweigh so great a sacrifice as to deny him the right to marry whom he chose.

The Dowager tearfully approached her 'goot Miss Chudleigh'.

'You were so successful in saving him from zat voman – zat Qvakeress can you not advice the King how it vould be wrongk for him to marry Lady Sarah? He must marry a Princess of ze bloodt Royal.'

Elizabeth thought but did not say that the King would be lucky to marry the adorable Sarah in preference to some plain and dumpy German girl, blood Royal or not, but she promised to advise the King that His Majesty's subjects might object to his choice.

'If by my subjects you mean my mother and Lord Bute,' George protruded a sulky lower lip, 'I don't give a –' he substituted the damn he was impiously about to say for 'give a, er – a jot to what anyone objects.'

Elizabeth's inventive faculties did not desert her.

'Sir, I have to tell you what I am loth to impart, yet I feel I ought to let you know I am acquainted with Lady Sarah. She is a most charming girl. I am also acquainted with her mother, the Duchess. She often comes to my entertainments.' This was true enough. There was neither a Duchess, nor a person of any rank who did not attend the Chudleigh's lavish entertainments at her Duke's expense. 'But I think Lady Sarah's affections are engaged elsewhere. She has, as your Majesty must realize, countless admirers and she is, I fear, already bespoken. Although she did confess to me that her greatest love is for no man but for her pet squirrel.'

This again was partly true, for Elizabeth had seen Sarah on one of her visits to the Duchess of Richmond, playing with her pet squirrel and her mother had smilingly said:

'She showers all her love on that creature in its cage, and has no thought of love for any one of her suitors except,' the Duchess had slyly added, 'one, the most eligible of them all.'

The strategy worked. George broken-heartedly declared he would not play second fiddle to any man alive and certainly not to a squirrel!

So Sarah would not be the King's Queen Consort after all. George took it hardly. He fell into a state of melancholic depression, a state that would always be a forerunner of mental instability in his later life.

'So intensely did I love her,' he is reported to have said, 'that I think my mind will not bear up against the shock of disappointment.'

His mind had to bear up because, in the following year, just before George was crowned, Sarah married Sir John Bunbury. That marriage proved a failure for her who would have been more content with her squirrel until she obtained a divorce, married George Napier and became the mother of two famous sons, Sir James and Sir William Napier.

George, having ceased to long for the unattainable, knew he would willy-nilly have to marry a Princess as urged by his dominant mother and his 'dear friend' Lord Bute. After much negotiation by Bute, and continued shock and disappointment on the part of George, a Princess was found for him by one Colonel Graham, a hardy Scot and faithful Jacobite whom Bute, himself a Scot and secret Jacobite also, had instructed to visit the German Courts with a view to finding a Princess for the King to marry.

The canny Scot chose wisely when he approached the Duke of Mecklenburg-Strelitz for the hand of his daughter Charlotte.

She was a plain, good and honest girl, if by 'good' we may liken her to George, the King, as given to hymn singing, prayer, and Bible readings. She could not have been more flattered at being singled out from all other German Princesses to be Queen Consort of King George the Third.

In the last week of August 1761 Princess Charlotte embarked for England. She brought with her two ladies in waiting, Frauen Hagedorn and Schwellenberg, the latter to remain in favour with the future Queen for all her married life. This lady came to be detested by the King's third son William,* who succeeded his brother George to their father's Throne more than sixty years later. Frau Schwellenberg collected pet toads, a singular hobby, which she kept in glass cages and would feed with flies and other savoury dainties.

With these two unattractive attendants Charlotte arrived in London after a dreadful voyage across the North Sea; but while her ladies lay groaning below, Charlotte suffered none of their agonies. She walked on the deck with the spray in her face and the wind in her hair, and to comfort her prostrate Schwellenberg and Hagedorn, she sang hymns.

It would have rejoiced the heart of George could he have seen and heard his bride so valiantly braving the elements and singing, not untunefully, his favourite hymns, in German, of course, for she could speak no English.

She was hideously dressed in blue quilted satin, her hair twisted into bunches of curls, but if a plain little girl – she had nondescript features, a large mouth full of teeth, all her own, and a smile widely stretched – she had youth on her side. She was just eighteen and Walpole had nothing more derogatory to say of her and her looks, except that 'she was pale and homely, her nose something flat, her mouth very large . . .' So large that Gillray, the caricaturist, cruelly sketched her face with its numerous teeth as that of a crocodile.

As she drove through the streets of the King's capital,
*See *Royal William*.

the roars of a multitudinous crowd greeted her, guns thundered their welcome, bells rang in church towers and, as the coach rumbled along Constitutional Hill:

'*Gott im Himmel!*' exclaimed the Schwellenberg. 'I am given no time to dress your Highness for the wedding.'

'The wedding?' said Charlotte, pale, 'not – my – not the King's wedding? Not – our – *my* wedding?'

'Yes, Highness, your wedding – tonight,' replied the Schwellenberg who nursed on her ample knees a cage with her favourite toad asleep on a silken cushion.

Her wedding! That night . . . 'God,' she prayed, 'make me worthy.'

Her bridegroom, as nervous as was she, met her at the gate of St James's Palace. For an almost imperceptible moment he drew back before he raised her from her curtsy and, as she made as if to kneel in homage, he came forward, forced a smile to his face – for she was indeed plain and looked even more so in her ugly dress and those bunches of curls – but remembering his duty, he raised her up, kissed her, a peck on her pale cheek, and led her into his palace.

That same evening the courtiers assembled in their finery, among them the ubiquitous Horace who, after the wedding ceremony had been duly performed by the Archbishop, had noted, with his customary eulogy to Royalty: 'The Queen looks very sensible, cheerful, and is remarkably genteel. Her tiara of diamonds was very pretty.' Which is more than he can say of Charlotte, but he compromised by describing her stomacher as 'sumptuous; her violet mantle of ermine so heavy that the spectators knew as much of her upper half as the King himself . . . They did not get to bed till two.'

When we can take it that the King knew more of her upper half than did the spectators, or he, had previously observed.

Nevertheless, and in spite of his first recoil at sight of her, George was soon to be happy with his bride whose admirable qualities, her prudishness, her amiability, and her dislike of all the flagrant delights of his grandfather's Court, matched his own, all but her inexcusable fondness for the awful Schwellenberg and her horrible toads. George was utterly defeated by the Schwellenberg. She was there and there she must remain in full possession of Charlotte.

We may be sure Elizabeth did not share, or appear to share, the general dismay of George's subjects at the 'remarkable gentility' ascribed to the Queen by Walpole. The Sovereign's people had expected, if not a beauty, at least a Queen Consort of some distinction, not a homely, plain, timid young girl who could not speak English, only tolerable French. But Charlotte was soon to prove less timid when she conducted herself with admirable dignity at the Coronation, at which we may be sure Elizabeth was present and had a seat of honour, if not with the peeresses with other persons of high degree.

She continued to be the favourite of the Princess Dowager second only to H.R.H.'s 'goot Lord Bute', against whom scurrilous broadsides were directed by a riotous mob, his chair attacked, his life endangered. Elizabeth who, as everyone knew, was loyal to the Princess and emphatically contradicted all these ugly rumours, deemed it wiser to keep clear of London. Mobs were rising against Bute who was soon to oust Pitt, and having got rid of the ineffectual Lord Newcastle got himself made Prime Minister, the King's 'dear Friend'.

And now George was brought into bad odour, thought to be a mere tool in the hands of a 'wanton widow, the Dowager Princess and her Scottish paramour'.

It took five years for the King to live this down and regain the respect of his people, during which time Elizabeth remained in virtual retirement from the Court yet always at command of the King's mother.

We hear of 'the Chudleigh' still giving lavish entertainments at her Knightsbridge house, still subsidized by her

Duke and still the 'Virgin Mistress', as Walpole would have it. The name stuck.

But all was not *couleur de rose* in Elizabeth's rose-coloured drawing-room with its beautiful brocade curtains and magnificent furnishings derided by Horace.

It may be remembered that a pretty little milliner had supplied Madam with hats and such-like accessories after the late King's death. That her 'Evie' could ever seek feminine attraction other than herself did not occur to Elizabeth as possible until it dawned upon her that her 'Evie' was evincing too much interest in the little milliner from Cranbourne Alley.

Elizabeth was not disposed to tolerate her Duke's fancy for a rival and did not scruple to tell him so.

'I understand you frequently visit my milliner to buy hats for me or for – whom?'

Kingston, very much taken aback, evinced surprise. 'I don't know what you mean – I –'

'You know very well what I mean. You have been seen in her shop. Do you think I'll stand by to have you befooled by a little slut who sells herself to any man willing to pay for her secondhand goods?'

'She,' feebly essayed his Grace, 'is a highly respectable woman. You do mistake her and – and my intentions. I only called on her,' gaining courage he extemporized, 'to see her – see her modes and –'

'Her modes!' was heatedly interrupted. 'Her modes of pleasuring you and other of her customers who seek variety of *modes* in their old age.'

That was a cruel cut, for Kingston had always been sensitive of his seniority in years to the lady of his choice.

'Not so – so old that I cannot pleasure you, my love.'

'You think? As much pleasure,' his love exploded, 'as from a jelly-fish. But if you want variety, go get it from her and be poxed! Do you believe you are the only visitor to whom she offers her *modes*?' And with that repeated emphasis, she laughed loudly and long, 'Aha-ha-hah! Go to her then and take what's coming to you. Modes and robes and fallals are not the only things she sells in Cranbourne Alley at a higher price than you'd pay in a bawdy house, so I'll leave you to her but not in my house.'

'Our house,' timidly ventured his Grace.

'*My* house in all but name since you bought it in your name for me. So go take her if you will but you won't have me. I'll leave her to you and I'll be off!'

'No, no!' Kingston, greatly alarmed, attempted placation. 'Do you think I would lose you for – for anyone, much less a common little doxy?'

'I do. But you might at least have picked on a woman of quality. There's half a dozen at Court, my sister Maids of Honour,' sneered Miss Chudleigh, 'who'd be only too willing to oblige . . . Keep away from me!' As he advanced, arms outstretched to take her. 'I've done with you. I'm for Carlsbad. My doctor,' she fabricated, 'orders me a course in the baths for a pain in my side. A pleurisy.'

'Surely not!' he exclaimed, alarm increasing. 'I had no idea you were in need of –'

'In no need of you at all events,' said she; and on that last word she flounced from the room, leaving him visibly appalled.

Of course the gossips had all to tell of that.

Walpole, first in the field with news of the Chudleigh's row with the Duke, gives us the cause of it.

'His Grace of Kingston has taken a pretty little milliner from Cranbourne Alley and carried her to Thorseby' (the Kingston family seat). Lady Mary Coke also gives her version of it, told with her usual malicious glee.

'Miss Chudleigh is going to wash herself in the baths of Bohemia. They will be very famous if they cure her from all her disorders.'

There were other speculations as to why the Chudleigh should have suddenly decided to take a cure at the Carlsbad baths. Lord Chesterfield, writing to his son who was in Germany at this time, tells him on whom Elizabeth called, for the younger Chesterfield had been one of her admirers as well as his father: 'Your guest, Miss Chudleigh, no more wanted the waters than you did. Is it to show the Duke of Kingston that he cannot live without her? A dangerous experiment.'

She did not give Kingston time enough to come to such conclusion if experiment or not; and that he took his little milliner to Thoresby is doubtful and more likely wishful thinking on the part of Horace, for there is no evidence that Kingston entertained any woman but Elizabeth at his country seat. Whether she did or did not cure herself of her disorders in the Carlsbad baths it is certain she made good use of her travels in Germany. We hear of her from Lady Mary Coke that: 'Miss Chudleigh was set out for Dresden to visit the Electress of Saxony . . .' Who, it seems, if Lady Mary is to be believed, 'has given her jewels of very considerable value'.

The Electress of Saxony was not her only royal patron for, according to reports of those gossip writers who record her adventures in their numerous letters to friends abroad, Elizabeth was favoured by both small and great Prussians, including Frederick the Great himself who, as he recalled it, was 'diverted at some dull function by Madame Chudleigh, when she staggered as she danced at this ball', which the Great Frederick did not enjoy until Madame, unused to the potency of Rhine wine, drank two bottles of it. This also is doubtful, if recorded by Lady Mary Coke, for Elizabeth was always a moderate drinker, but certain it is that Frederick the Great had been captivated by 'Madame Chudleigh', as also it seems was Casanova who arrived in Brunswick after Elizabeth had travelled from Carlsbad. Casanova reported that the Crown Prince of Prussia was present at a military display given in his honour (or could it have been in Elizabeth's honour?). However that may be, here we have Elizabeth among other distinguished visitors when it came on heavily to rain. 'Madame Chudleigh, dressed in light muslin, did not run for shelter as did the other ladies there, but insisted on watching the display. Clad,' as Casanova noted, 'in thin Indian muslin and very little else and was soaked to the skin that her clothes clung to her making her appear more than naked. . . .' Not for the first time she had appeared more than naked, if we remember the famous masquerade where she went dressed, or undressed, as Iphigenia.

Her tour ended in a blaze of triumph which occasioned more envy when reported to those in London who had followed her travels in Germany from eye witness friends of theirs and enemies of hers.

She returned to England via Calais to find her Duke cured of *his* 'disorder' and no more was seen or heard of the little milliner.

FIVE

Back again at the Knightsbridge house she found her
'Evie' adoring as ever and as always ready to oblige her
every whim and extravagant demands. So extravagant
and sumptuous were her entertainments that even the
Fortunatus purse of the Duke had found a hole in it. For
his generous allowance proved insufficient for her lavish
hospitality and the expenses for which he had paid during
her travels abroad with her three or four attendants and
her extensive wardrobe.

So now we hear of her running into debt to the tune
of five thousand pounds borrowed from Drummond's
bank, and another nineteen hundred from a Mr William
Field, attorney of the Inner Temple. Of course everyone
got wind of these debts and all wondered if they might
lead to a final termination of the Chudleigh's relationship
with Kingston. Would he pay up or let her go – to end, as
was hopefully suggested – in a debtor's prison ?

Nothing of the sort. Kingston paid up or, at any rate,
gave her more than sufficient of the allowance he had
previously made her, that she could settle with her
creditors.

Her mother, who had died some years before, had never
known of her marriage to Hervey, nor had she left her
daughter any money, as her income as Housekeeper at
Windsor sufficed for all her needs but no more than that.
It was just as well that Mrs Chudleigh had known nothing
of Elizabeth's marriage, which soon became the topic of
the day to take precedence over the Chudleigh's financial
affairs; for while it had been rumoured that the Chudleigh
had a husband somewhere or other, none had paid much

heed to it. But now it was in everybody's mouth that the Duke's 'Virgin Mistress', as Walpole delighted to call her, had been married for years – No, not to Kingston, no! Not to her Duke, much as she would have wished to be his Duchess. Yet the fact she was known to be otherwise wedlocked . . . speculation hesitated. But to whom?

Yet after a while that absorbing question ceased to buzz around the Court since another name was in everybody's mouth, the name of Wilkes.

A disturber of political peace this Wilkes, having married a wealthy wife several years his senior, exploited himself, on her money, as a fashionable rake and a candidate for Parliament. Worse than that, much worse, he founded a rag known as the *North Briton* in which he trained a volley of abuse at Bute, who had succeeded Pitt as Prime Minister. There were nods and winks at Bute's elevation, knowing him to be not only the King's 'dear friend' but the King's mother's 'dearest friend'.

George, happily married to his plain little Charlotte, who in the last two years had borne him a Prince of Wales and a Duke of York, found that if all was quiet on his domestic front of St James's Palace it was anything but quiet outside his Palace walls.

We know George had been a pious, dutiful, honest and good little boy as Prince of Wales and also when first as King; but now grown to manhood his streak of obstinacy had grown with him so that we see him not only as the founder of a family with a future Heir to his Throne but as an autocrat and bigot who firmly believed in the Divine Right of Kingship, a right by which he chose to govern his people and his Heir.

We may therefore imagine His Majesty's horrified reactions to Wilkes's denunciation of the King's 'Divinely Right' speech from the Throne as: 'The most abandoned instance of ministerial effrontery ever imposed on mankind.'

Whereupon offended Majesty ordered a warrant for the

arrest of Wilkes and had him packed off to the Tower for treasonable libel. . . .

Now this Wilkes had not only half the country behind him but almost half the women of the Court, which is the more surprising as he was hideous and cross-eyed, yet possessed of a certain charm that women and even some men found irresistible. Whether Elizabeth found him irresistible we are in no position to say, but it is most likely that she failed to fall a victim to his charm, however much he may have squinted at her to catch her eye, since he had no title and was detested by the Dowager Princess for having done his worst to her 'goot Lord Bute', besides having vilified the King, her son.

Yet Wilkes was not to be outdone by a young Majestic autocrat. With public opinion declaring him to have been unjustly condemned and this, besides the average man in the street, included a good many of Bute's rivals in Parliament, and the cry 'Wilkes, Liberty, and the Forty-Five' (so called because it was the forty-fifth number of his scurillous rag, the *North Briton*, that had attacked Bute) was yelled in every gutter.

Things were looking serious; George had a brainstorm and his mother asked Elizabeth, to whom she would turn for advice in any difficulty: 'Vat, O, vat are ve to do?'

Elizabeth advised her what to do.

So, when brought up for trial in the Court of Common Pleas, Wilkes was granted heavy damages for false imprisonment and immediate release. But Wilkes thought it better to lie low for a while until the storm raging round his name had subsided. He therefore went off to France and stayed there until the dawn of a general election, when he returned to London.

Although to the King the name of Wilkes was a synonym for Satan, the Dowager Princess more than ever held her 'Goot Elizabet' in high esteem. According to the Dowager she had saved the King from, as she put it, 'a vicked Revolution' by advising His Majesty, or rather the

114

Dowager Princess, to persuade George not to pursue the trial of Wilkes but to agree to his release.

'Ze people,' his mother warned him, 'vouldt have rise against you if Wilkes hadt not von his case. You shouldt be t'ankful to Miss Chudleigh for her advice to me.'

If the King were not so thankful to Miss Chudleigh as was his mother for the release of Wilkes, the mob went raving mad with excitement. Wilkes had become their hero, their champion, a forerunner of Paine with his *Rights of Man* some two decades later. They paraded the streets smashing the windows of all houses suspect of being anti-Wilkes. Wonder it was that the Queen's house, Buckingham House, afterwards Buckingham Palace, was not attacked.

So for the next three or four years until the general election the King and his Government under the useless Lord Rockingham, who had followed Bute as Premier, had no immediate cause for alarm. The monster Wilkes who, for the King, incorporated the devil and all his imps in his squint-eyed sub-human form, was, as George fervently prayed, outlawed for ever, as good as dead and burning in the hell from which he had arisen. And now . . . horror of all horrors! Wilkes was back again. Defiant of authority, outlawry and the King, and with his rowdy mob at his heels, he had the audacity to stand as candidate for the City of London. Defeated in this first attempt he stood as Member for Brentford in Middlesex and won with a huge majority.

If his bawling followers had been wildly elated when he was vindicated and released from prison, the return of their hero and his victory as a Member of Parliament became a riot of rejoicing. As before, windows were smashed, and the house of Bute in South Audley Street had not a pane of glass left. It was an invasion. 'Mob rule', as the harassed King's Government decided. But what was to be done? Short of another imprisonment or, if George had his way, execution, there was nothing to be done. You could not imprison a Member of Parliament, much less hang him unless proved guilty of treason.

What a ghastly predicament for the Government, and a nightmare for the King! The first signs of mental instability became a cause of anxiety to his doctors, the bloodshot eyes, the perpetual repetition of 'What, What – What is to do? This Wilkes – this demon – this – this –' Words failed him. Wilkes had become an obsession. 'Get him out – out – out!'

He was temporarily got out and handed over to the Marshal of the King's Bench prison. More riots from his mob, more yelling and execrations hurled at George, now in a pitiable state. 'Wilkes and Liberty!' was the cry at every street corner and worse than that: 'Wilkes and no King!'

The Grenadier Guards were commanded from the Palace, and when the Riot Act was read, the crowd merely shouted derision. But Wilkes remained in prison and from there strove to calm his rioters.... 'The time for action had not come!' So did he try to make himself heard from his barred windows.

During all these alarms and excursions Elizabeth and her Duke had remained, as far as could be possible, immune from the violent exploits of Wilkes's howling supporters. Knightsbridge was well on the way to Brentford where Wilkes had won his famous victory, and the house of Wilkes in Kensington Gore was no distance from Kingston's house in Knightsbridge, which had become the scene of further violence. But Bute's house was their target, across Hyde Park to the Kingston mansion.

In vain did Elizabeth's 'Evie' implore her to remain indoors. 'To show yourself outside these walls is asking for attack. The mob are fighting mad.' She would not listen.

'If there's any fighting to be done I'd like to see it. Not since Cromwell has London been involved in revolution.'

'Revolution!' The Duke's red gills paled. 'What nonsense is this! There's no revolution, only a vulgar rabble out to force the Government to release this dastardly Wilkes from prison. He is a danger to the community, and if you will take heed of me – which, my love, you never do – you will stay at home until all this is over.'

The Duke apparently realized that the last thing his 'love' would heed was advice from him. She thought of it all as an exciting entertainment. She was always fearless of personal danger, and her sympathies were not wholly against Wilkes. That the mob, the people of the lower world who starved in poverty, had found a champion for their cause to right their wrongs, seemed to her not so much an outrage as a protest against the difference between the lot of those born in an underworld where starvation and oppression prevailed, and those of her world where the price she paid for one of her hats would have kept a starving family in food for a month.

That the young sovereign had gained the respect of his people by his careful maintenance of the proprieties in contrast to the orgies practised at the Courts of his father, his grandfather and great-grandfather, of which the prudishness inherent in Elizabeth had disapproved, also enabled her to see both sides of the picture, notwithstanding her reverence for titles, as great as Walpole's own. He, unlike Elizabeth, could never see nor wish to see one side of a picture if it showed the drab and muddy stains of poverty and oppression of a common herd as far removed from Walpole's life as heaven is from hell.

So we see her driving out in her coach straight into the midst of the crowds that were stampeding toward the prison where Wilkes had been detained until it was decided what to do with him. Was he or was he not to remain a Member of Parliament?

Elizabeth's excitement increased, although she knew that these demonstrations from a herd of wild beasts, as they seemed to her, were regardless of any law or discipline. 'Drive on!' she called to her coachman, for he had halted to send one of her footmen to ask if Madam would go back. 'Drive on!' again she bade the footman who looked scared. 'Do you not hear me? Drive *on*!'

But even as he climbed back to his place, some of the crowd rushed forward, bawling and brandishing banners inscribed: 'Wilkes and Liberty!'

They wore blue cockades in their hats, Wilkes's insignia, and as they advanced upon the coach, Elizabeth wished she had not insisted that the driver should go on and not back.... Too late now! They had forced their way through their howling fellows; grinning ugly faces peered in at the windows, some had chalk in their grubby hands and were scribbling on the paintwork of the doors, 45 – the fatal number of the *North Briton*'s issue that had started all this with Wilkes's virulent attack on the King's speech and his Government. Insults were hurled at her. 'See the Duke's Virgin Mistress!' ... How could the rabble know of Walpole's name for her? What didn't they know? They must have their spies among our own servants, she thought frantically.... And now she saw that some of them were carrying, besides their banners, torches held high – and this was too awful – they were lighting squibs in a series of small explosions that the street ran in little rivulets of flame. Stones were thrown at windows of the houses along the road, some of which were presumed to be anti-Wilkes, and more squibs flung helter-skelter just for the fun of it by hooligan boys. One of these shattered the glass of her coach window and set light to the lace hem of her gown. Stifling a scream she had the presence of mind to stamp out a trickle of fire at her feet and, seizing a cushion from behind her, she crushed the lighted lace that edged her hooped petticoats. ... 'Madam!' her footman had opened the door of the coach, 'Are you hurt?'

'I might have been burnt to death if they had their way.' She managed to laugh off her fright. 'You can tell him to go back now – if he can.'

The coachman lashed with his whip at the hurtling mob. They had now run berserk and were throwing squibs, stones, bricks, and yelling execrations at her, at her coachman, and at the carriages that followed in the mêlée until, taking fright at the trampling horses that would have stampeded along with the crowd, they dispersed terror-stricken, helter-skelter with cries of 'Break! Break!' 'The military!...' Sure enough a company of Guards, the Grenadiers, were marching to the rescue.

'They are naught but a lot of cowardly curs,' she told her pale footman. 'I'd be glad to see them all trundled off to Tyburn. On, then, on!'

So on went her coach, scattering the mob in full flight, and came at last to the gates of her Duke's mansion.

Some of his windows, she saw, had suffered breakage but none that could not easily be repaired.

Kingston was waiting for her in a near apoplexy. 'Thank God! Thank God!' He was blubbering with relief. 'I begged you not to go ... Good Heavens ... your face!'

'What's the matter with my face?' She ran to a mirror on the wall to see that the smoke from the torches and the squibs had caused a blackened film to spread across her cheeks. 'That's the least of it. My lace is in ribbons – scorched beyond redemption.'

And to the Duke's valet, Whitehead, who had noiselessly approached: 'Tell my woman to come to me.'

He bowed with mock servility. 'Very good – hem – madam.'

This Whitehead was a sly, furtive fellow who had been in the service of the Duke for some ten years. By various unuttered words he had let her know he would take no orders from her whose presence in his Grace's houses he regarded as the intrusion of a woman who had as much right to be there as in a brothel. She had put up with his veiled insolence rather than cause her 'Evie' unnecessary worry, for she knew he relied on this beast of a Whitehead, as to herself she thought of him who would not hesitate to have her out had he his way. But she was biding her time which would come just so soon as she could have *her* way – and get *him* out.

She watched him go, his head high and his thin, inquisitive nose pointed in the direction of the servants' hall. He walked with leisurely tread, his back in its dark, close-fitting broadcloth expressing the disdain he felt for her who had possession of his Grace, and whom he doubted not would be *her* Grace if by any intricate cunning means she would succeed in what he knew to be her obsessive aim. He was a man of some education, and in a sheaf of letters he had written which were published after her death did much to besmirch her memory to the delight of her enemies.

It is hard to believe that Elizabeth Chudleigh should have made so many enemies, for she was a good-natured creature. Her only fault, if so small a fault it were, being her love of a title, a sense of 'grandness', which was less *folie de grandeur* than the desire for power, to be able to gratify her every whim, a thousand extravagances, servants galore, her black page boys to be dressed in garish liveries as her personal pets, carelessly to drain the resources of her Duke. Yet she had come to love him – not a passionate love as he loved her, rather that of a maternal tenderness despite she was much his junior in years.

So, seeing his anxiety on her behalf that looked to bring about a temporary collapse for he would worry himself sick over trivialities, she consulted Caesar Hawkins.

'When he gets excited the veins of his forehead thicken and stand out in ridges,' she had told Hawkins. 'What does that signify?'

'Overheated blood,' he had informed her. 'His Grace needs to lead a quiet peaceable life. He is paying for too lively a youth.'

'I never knew him in his youth,' she said, and thought:

120

'If only I had! Even though I would have been but eight when he was twenty. . . .'

'Madam' (her maid, or one of them, she had three always at her beck and call, had come to her) 'wishes me to attend her?'

'Yes, I have been caught in a storm. Thunder and lightning. Look at my gown.'

'Oh, madam, gracious goodness!' exclaimed the girl. 'Your lace!'

'Yes, it is sadly the worse for a – a burning. I'll to my room if your Grace,' to the agitated Duke, whom she always addressed before the servants as if on the least familiar terms, 'will excuse me.'

She curtsied as she left him. It was recognized that her visits to the Duke's houses and frequent entertainments given by her were at his request, he having no womenfolk to act as hostess; she had even hinted that the Duke, a friend of her late father, had left his orphaned daughter in his Grace's charge while still a child – this to be spread about the servants' hall and retailed to circumvent gossip. If the staff took this improbability for the little it was worth, it sufficed for them, with the exception of Whitehead, to accept it.

In the hands of her maid, bathed, robed and her ruined gown given to her – 'Make such use of it as you will. It is useless to me.'

'Oh, madam, and brand new, the first time worn. I can mend the lace.'

'No, you can have it or give it to the scavengers.' What did it matter to her or to 'Evie' that the lace alone had cost him twenty guineas, being real rose point? Her maid could sell it if she wished.

And now we have something to tell of this particular maid, whose name was also Elizabeth.

Some several years ago when the mother of our Elizabeth was housekeeper at Windsor, an infant girl had been deposited at the door of Mrs Chudleigh's apartments in the Castle. A foundling with no message, no letter, nothing to tell whence she came and to whom she belonged.

Mrs Chudleigh, having made inquiries and finding no trace of the baby's mother, took the child into her care, brought her up as if she were her own and ran the gauntlet of suspicion attached, not to herself for she was past child-bearing age, but to her daughter.

'The Chudleigh', always the target for mud-slinging, disdained all aspersions flung at her; and when her mother died she took the girl, then about fourteen, into her own charge. From then on she was always a favourite attendant of her lady, for whom she had been named.

So here was another sharp-edged innuendo to dig at the much-maligned Chudleigh who, when Nemesis descended upon her, gave her a bastard daughter of a father unknown and a son who might or might not have been Hervey's, since he had known nothing of the birth and death of Elizabeth's child, supposedly born in wedlock.

After the hullabaloo caused by Wilkes and his 'Sons of Liberty' subsided, Elizabeth, defiant of perpetual talk still noised around her 'friendship' with Kingston to say naught of her marriage with Hervey, which for some time had been no longer a secret, was at the height of her triumphal career.

Although her detractors persisted in furnishing every scrap of spite against her in their letters to their many correspondents, she flaunted her conquest of Kingston undeterred by the malice of Lady Mary Coke or the scrupulously critical and catty Mr Walpole.

We learn from Lady Mary that 'the Chudleigh' as they still insisted in preserving her maiden name, giving every hint she had no right to it, 'continues with her lavish entertainments and is invited to a ball held by the King and Queen,' . . . much to the dismay of Lady Mary.

Elizabeth attended the Princess Dowager who was beaming satisfaction to see her George no longer in dread lest he be dethroned, or worse, beheaded by that Monster Wilkes. The Princess had endured the torment of appalling apprehension, having studied the history of her son's royal heritage and remembered how his remote ancestor, the first Stuart King Charles, had his head cut off by a revolutionary – 'dat so schokink Cromvell which might – *Gott im Himmel!* have been the fate of George!'

Lady Mary Coke notes, with what disgust may be imagined, that 'The Chudleigh danced in company with their Majesties'. . . . We can hardly think that either Her Majesty, Queen Charlotte, heavy with carrying yet another prince, or the Princess Dowager, being past her dancing years, would have danced with anyone at all. Yet if Lady Mary had seen the Chudleigh dancing with the King it could have been to her as great a sacrilege as if Jezebel had been seen dancing with one of the Archangels.

'Such are the times,' deplores Lady Mary, and goes on to relate how the Chudleigh in discussing a recent marriage of a spinster, Lady Susan Stewart, in her fifties, 'Since she has got a husband I don't think any of us old maids need despair . . .' '*Us* old maids!' crows Lady Mary, 'isn't that charming?'

By which it is evident that not only Lady Mary but Horace Walpole and everybody else who claimed to know that the Duke's 'Virgin Mistress' was, as she mischievously informed the industrious chronicler, Mary Coke, no longer an 'Old Maid'. That started both Horace and Mary on a race between them to be first in the field with the news that Hervey was suing for a divorce!

Lady Mary won.

'Mr Hervey is going to prove his marriage as the first stage to sue for being unmarried and has sent the lady who goes by the name of 'Miss Chudleigh' a letter to signify his intention. To which it appears she returned the reply that if he proves his marriage he will have to pay £16,000 as she owes that sum of money. . . .'

This is sheer guess work on the part of Mary Coke for Kingston had already paid all of her debts, nor had Elizabeth made any such condition; nor, as reported, had Hervey sent her any such letter. Invention or wishful thinking both by Horace and Mary Coke. Walpole, not to be outdone, also confirms that 'The Nymph' (his latest name for her) 'has sent word to Hervey that he must pay her debts which looks as if she is not sure of being the Duchess of Kingston. . . .'

This is the only positive assumption in the whole tissue of talk or tissue of lies concocted against the 'Nymph Chudleigh' by these two, Walpole and Mary Coke, who both hated her. Why? We know Horace bore her a grudge from their childhood days when, with premature precocity, she had jibed at him for that which she had picked up from her mother's gossips visiting Chelsea House, concerning Walpole's birth. 'Who's your father?' . . . It had rankled all these years and this may well have been a reason for this inimitable scribe's malicious interest in Elizabeth Chudleigh. But why should Mary Coke go to such lengths to make her the butt of her scribbles sent round to all her intimates and handed down to malign her for the garbage-mongers of the hot news columnists?

Mary's reason for spending much ink and time as to whether the Chudleigh were married or not, is nothing less than jealousy of her, who was received at the Courts, not only of the Dowager Princess who held her in highest favour but by the King and Queen. As the year of the Wilkes disturbance drew to its close with Wilkes, if not forgotten, no longer a nightmarish menace to George, Elizabeth is honoured by an invitation to a ball held at St James's. And Mary Coke, not invited, is told by one who was that: 'The young Princess danced with The Chudleigh.' What Princess could have danced with the Chudleigh is again a matter of incredibility since the eldest daughter of Queen Charlotte was but two years old.

The Queen, with perennial regularity, had borne her husband in their six years of marriage five children and would
bear him several more, two dying as infants and two of
them, the King's eldest son George, born in 1762, and his
third son William, born in 1765, both destined to be
Kings of Great Britain and Ireland.

It must have been as great a disappointment to Mary
Coke and to Horace Walpole that, in spite of rumours of
divorce between the married, or unmarried Chudleigh,
Elizabeth went happily on her glorified way as the
Princess Dowager's 'goot Elizabet' and the King's 'good
friend'. He had always been grateful to her for guiding
him out of the mess he got into with the Lightfoot Quaker
girl, although he was not quite so grateful that, indirectly
through his good friend Mistress Chudleigh's interven-
tion, he had lost the beloved Sarah Lennox. But if he
had won her he would never have had his Charlotte for
Consort.

His devotion to and affection for his ugly little wife
was a continuous source of amusement to his Court, not
unmixed with annoyance and incessant boredom. Because
the Queen was almost always pregnant with a prince or
princess – another source of grins and chuckles from the
men and wonder from the women as to how the King
could bring himself to couple with so unattractive a
bedmate and with such effectual result. But that couple
he did and with evident enjoyment and success went a
long way to increase his unpopularity among his courtiers
and, conversely, to make him the more popular with the
lower and middle classes of his subjects. Here at last was
a true and sincere Defender of the Faith, a pillar of
respectability, a father of a family like any one of them,
who held marriage to be a sacrament and to whom not
one breath of scandal could ever be attached.

The banishment of splendour, extravagance (the King
was known to be frugal, his favourite dish boiled mutton
with caper sauce and turnips) and no illicit intrigues with

half a dozen mistresses on whom to waste his or his Government's money, occasioned much discontent among those who had enjoyed the saturnalian revels of the old King's Court.

Elizabeth may have sometimes wished for a little more excitement than the Queen's page, Albert Papendiek, playing his flute, or the King listening to the music of Handel, with the Queen's appalling Hagedorn and Schwellenberg, the latter nursing on her ample knees a cage with one of her revolting toads inside it, and all of them sitting round in a dreary circle. Yet she never admitted, except to her inner self, anything but fervent appreciation of these deadly boring entertainments.

And it is now for the first time since that secret marriage, or what passed for a marriage so many years before, that Augustus Hervey appears at the Court of St James's.

Of course, he had from time to time been seen in the company of the late King's entourage and had also been sighted – at a distance – by Elizabeth who had been careful to keep out of his way, and he equally out of hers on his short leaves from his naval occasions. Hervey, however much a failure as a husband, was an unqualified success as a naval officer. His service in the Navy with England continuously at war had kept him out of the country for long periods at a time. He had been engaged in the capture of Havannah in 1762 and later promoted Captain Commander of the Mediterranean Fleet. Whenever he did get leave to come to London he made not the slightest attempt to see or communicate with his wife, or with the woman he had secretly married, if a marriage it were.

Hervey's reappearance at the Court of St James's was the primary cause of the Coke-*cum*-Walpole united spread of news concerning Hervey's intention to sue for a divorce.

Elizabeth, while preserving the utmost discretion in her

relationship with Kingston, began to be uneasy as to what Hervey really intended to do.

Because the Earl of Bristol seemed quite to have regained his health, Elizabeth racked her brains and passed sleepless nights how to prove she had never been married to Hervey since the witnesses of that secret ceremony at midnight in the dark little chapel were all dead. So what to do? . . . She again consulted Caesar Hawkins, who had known of the birth of her child. But although she had called herself Mrs Hervey, Hawkins had only her word for it that Hervey was the father of her son. Hawkins had much experience in attending the births of infants born to Maids of Honour, and was tactful enough not to probe too deeply into the parentage of the babes he had brought into the world.

'In any case,' Elizabeth told the sympathetic Hawkins, 'it was all such a scrambled affair, how can I know if it were a marriage or not?'

'Was there no register of the marriage?' Hawkins asked her.

'I believe . . .' she did some rapid thinking. She had been sent out of the room when that lawyer – what was his name? – had brought what he called a check book or something . . . 'yes, there was some sort of a register. I think I had better go and see Mr Merrill.'

She did not let Hawkins know that Merrill was almost certainly dead, and also the old clergyman, but she had made up her mind what to do and if there were a register of any evidence, because what she had heard at the keyhole of the door when all that business with a 'check book' had been discussed and decided who should take charge of it, was scarcely evidence.

'Yes. I can go to Lainston and make sure,' she told the surgeon, 'if there is a register.'

She left it at that with the approval of Hawkins, and was soon on her way by coach to Lainston House in the parish of Sparsholt.

Here again we have contradictory reports of Elizabeth's visit to Lainston, but if we are to believe that the *'Authentic Particulars'* are correct we may assume that Elizabeth, determined by hook and possible crook, having arrived at Lainston House and ascertained that the clergyman, Mr Amis, had died as also had Merrill, brought her ingenuity to bear upon her case to find a satisfactory means to end her marriage with Hervey.

She recalled that Merrill had volunteered to take the 'check book' into his care, but where it was now she had no idea. She ultimately traced that a parish register book had been placed in the parish church. There she went to that same little chapel where the secret ceremony had been performed before witnesses, all dead.

All dead, that is to say, except Anne Craddock. Elizabeth had entirely forgotten that she had been a witness if not to the wedding, at least to the bride and bridegroom apparently wedded and certainly bedded.

Confident that she could dispose of any evidence that she and Hervey were legally husband and wife, Elizabeth takes herself off to find the parish clerk.

A young and thoroughly incompetent youth was he, much impressed by the lady who drove up to the Chapel in an elegant post-chaise, obviously one of the 'Quality' to the clerk's unaccustomed eyes, he having seen none so elegant as she who addressed him with insinuating grace:

'Sir, would it be at all within your province to oblige me by inquiring – that is, to have a glance through the register book of births, marriage and deaths in this parish for the years 1744 and 1745? I am making investigations concerning a, er, a relative of mine who I have reason to believe died some –' calculation supplied the imperceptible pause – 'some twenty years ago.' (Because naturally, she reflected, any register of a death would also be registered in the same year as a marriage – and *her* marriage, pray God!)

It was the clerk's turn to hesitate.

He had recently been promoted to this insignificant office with a mere pittance of a salary, but he would not wish to lose his job and the ten shillings a week that went with it. Seeing his uncertainty, she turned the full battery of her charm upon him.

'I would be only too grateful for your assistance in this matter for I do wish to make sure that my relative – an old uncle of mine –' she omitted to give the name of Merrill who we know was not her uncle but a cousin once removed – 'did die in this parish, and if I may examine the registers of the years 1744 or 1745 I will pay the necessary fee.' That Merrill had died only one year ago was no concern of the clerk's.

'There is no fee, madam, but if you desire to see the register –'

'No fee! But I insist on paying, if not a fee a small gratuity for your obligement!'

She produced a purse and five golden guineas. The clerk's eyes devoured the sight of so much largesse. 'A small gratuity, indeed.' If the lady regarded five guineas as small what would she consider to be large? This ran through his mind as bowing low to her, his hand closed on the offering. . . . A bribe? went through his thoughts. If open to bribe, where would he stand if it were discovered he had accepted? . . .

'It is quite usual,' she said, seeing his hesitation, 'to pay for a reference in the register of births, marriages and deaths. I have made other inquiries in Winchester –' how easy to concoct these fabrications! – 'but have been referred to you here at Lainston. All, I assure you, is quite in order.'

So much in order, and with those five guineas transferred to his pocket, the clerk conducted his beautiful and wealthy visitor to the vestry. 'Here is the register, madam.' He offered for her inspection the ledger of the years required.

'Oh,' she exclaimed, glancing up and at a window on

the far side of the vestry, 'how strange to see a – a stork on the roof of that house,' she pointed vaguely. 'You know what they say about the arrival of a stork to a house? So you may soon expect another birth to register.' She laughed and so did he as he stood at the window searching for the alleged stork and saying: 'I did not know they had storks in this country.'

'Perhaps,' she said, 'it has flown from Denmark or somewhere.'

It took some time to leaf through the marriages under the dates indicated. And while chattering away at his turned back, she related an amusing story to do with how when she was a child she had asked her mother who had brought her baby brother to their house (we know she never had a brother) and was told the stork had brought him and she had always thought he had been found under a gooseberry bush.

While his attention was thus disengaged, she tore out the page containing the record of her marriage, tucked it into the bosom of her gown and said:

'I have found what I wanted to know. My uncle did die in the year 1744. I am grateful to you, sir. You see' (confidentially), 'I am acting on behalf of a claimant to part of my uncle's estate. A young impoverished cousin of mine recently come from, er, from the Indies. And now I can positively acquaint him with the date of my uncle's death – his great-uncle it would be – so that he may consult an attorney regarding the will of the deceased.'

The clerk, satisfied of her good intent and still more satisfied with her 'small gratuity', bowed her to the door and watched her drive away. He then went off to the inn to drink a toast to her and to himself and his good fortune.

Little did she guess nor could the clerk have guessed that the widow of the Rev. Mr Amis had remarried and was the wife of a butler who had been in the service of the Duke of Kingston, and that she, now Mrs Phillips, had retained the original register or 'check book', as it was called by the attorney, Mr Spearing, who had advised the record of the marriage to be placed in the charge of Mr Merrill. But Merrill, to be on the safe side in case the record should be lost, had handed the book over to the new incumbent of Sparshot parish. He immediately began to keep a register of births, marriages and deaths, which had never before been kept at Lainston Chapel. Having copied the register of the marriage of Hon. Augustus Hervey to Elizabeth Chudleigh, signed Thomas Amis, he gave back the original 'check book' to Merrill, who handed it into the keeping of Mrs Amis. But at that time she thought no more of it, until when eventually it came to light it was to bring about Elizabeth's undoing.

However, as she could not foresee what lay before her in the years ahead, she returned to London cheerfully confident that the damning evidence of the 'scrambled affair', as she had described her marriage to Caesar Hawkins, was disposed of for ever.

Back again at Knightsbridge she went to her room, took the leaf she had extracted from the register and burnt it in the fire.

She knelt to watch the flames curl the paper into grey and blackened ashes, no word of it visible. 'Dust and ashes,' she murmured and, still kneeling, sent up a prayer of thankfulness to God who had saved her from the monstrous travesty of what should have been and now could never be a marriage.

She was free of Hervey and when she should choose, for now she *could* choose, to marry Evelyn Pierrepoint and be his legal wife – the Duchess of Kingston.

SIX

After all these manoeuvres to disprove her marriage
with Hervey, she had not yet let her 'Evie' know she was
free of her encumbrance, for she wanted to be sure he
was still as determined as ever to marry her. She, ever
cautious, would not again run the risk of being 'jilted',
until too late she discovered that, thanks to her aunt's
interception of her lover's letters, she could have been
Hamilton's wife. But because of the little milliner episode,
and Kingston being of an age when he might think twice
about cementing their relationship, as he had latterly
appeared to be quite content with conditions as they
were, she was waiting until he should exert pressure upon
her to be his wife. She had waited so long she could wait
a little longer.

An injudicious decision, to give her a scarifying shock!
Because having, as she thought, destroyed the evidence of
her marriage to Hervey, she learned that the Earl of
Bristol, who years ago had been dying and recovered his
health, was now at Death's door. So that she could still
be a peeress even if she did not live with her husband as
his wife. And here again does Caesar Hawkins come to her
aid, acting as go-between in the interests of the Herveys.

As Court Surgeon he was an inveterate busy-body as
were all connected with the Courts of the Dowager
Princess and the King and Queen, but their Majesties had
very little use for him, preferring their own medical
attendants to those of their predecessor.

The news that Hawkins had to impart threw Elizabeth
into a ferment of frustration and anxiety. Her husband,
Hervey, was anxious to remarry and therefore he could

sue her for divorce, citing the Duke of Kingston as co-respondent.

While she had known of the rumours spread by the Mary Coke-*cum*-Walpole contingent that Hervey wished to divorce her, she had ignored these stray wisps of straw on the winds of malicious gossip levelled at her through so many years, serene in the favour of the Dowager Princess. But now that Hervey's definite intention had been made clear to her by Hawkins, it caused her to regret her previous device of destroying the evidence of her marriage to him. After all she could, if he failed to divorce her, be a Countess, if not a Duchess, and in any case to bring her Duke into so unsavoury a business as divorce, to that she would never agree. Her poor old devoted 'Evie'.

'Good God!' she exclaimed when Hawkins, pompously urbane, propounded to her Hervey's determination. 'Does he imagine I would agree to any such a disgraceful condition to dissolve a marriage that has never taken place?'

'Never?' Hawkins's eyebrows shot up to his white-powdered wig. 'My dear Mrs Hervey, consider. You would have some difficulty in disproving your marriage, despite, as you tell me, there is no evidence of any register of this marriage.

Here was a thunderbolt fallen from what she had thought to be a blue unclouded sky!

'But there *is* evidence,' she told him, controlling her voice that shook a very little. 'There was evidence at the time with witnesses present, only after so many years such evidence might have been lost. I did go to Lainston and inquired of the clerk of the parish but there was no register of the year 1744 – the year of my supposed marriage to Hervey – because the Chapel where the ceremony took place had no register.' (That at least was true.) 'I can, however, produce witnesses of the marriage.' (All dead she might have added, except Anne Craddock, and she didn't witness the wedding.)

'You can tell Hervey, who will, I suppose, be the Earl of Bristol today, tomorrow or any tomorrow in the next few weeks or months, that I refuse to submit to a divorce and that the marriage, if such it was, had never been consummated. Tell him that from me, and you can also tell him that if he persists in this outrageous demand, I will fight it and him to the bitter end. There is much you do not know to do with the night of our marriage which he would never wish to be brought to light in a Court of Law. He would be dismissed from the Navy, shunned by every man and woman in the land and out of it! Tell him I'll see him in hell where he deserves to be if he dares to bring a case of divorce against me and to cite the Duke of Kingston, that most honourable and noble peer –' she cast her eyes to heaven, a never-failing solicitation to which, *in extremis*, she would histrionically appeal ' – between whom and myself has never, despite the scurrilous reports that have made us both the subject of the garbage-mongers' mud slinging – never, I repeat, has our relationship been anything other than devoted friendship. The Duke has known of my marriage, as also does Her Royal Highness whom I have the honour to serve, and both she and the Duke have respected my secret. But because his Grace, as Brutus, is an honourable man, he has never taken advantage of the respect and love I bear him. Let Hervey try and prove otherwise. Go tell him this!'

Hawkins, never at a loss for diplomacy, was not at all anxious to carry such a message to him who might any day be entitled to the earldom of Bristol with some further advantage to Hawkins. Who knew if a peer in the Upper House might not obtain for him a knighthood since the present King, as Hawkins judged, had no use for him and would never bestow such an honour upon his grandfather's Court Surgeon. He therefore suggested another course.

134

Thus it came about that the Herveys, Augustus and Elizabeth, met after having been cautioned by Hawkins that the utmost secrecy must be maintained as to their meeting lest the outcome of a case, whether it went in the favour or disfavour of either party, should be judged as collusion.

The meeting which, in accordance with the instructions of Hawkins, took place at the house of Augustus Hervey situated close to the house in Conduit Street where Elizabeth had used to reside.

She went in some trepidation as to how he would receive her and what she might expect from him when she remembered their last meeting and the result of it, now dead and buried, their son of whom he knew nothing. He had no proof of the birth of Henry Augustus so he would be unable to prove consummation of their marriage even could he prove it had ever taken place.

Contrary to her apprehensive expectation, he met her with the utmost courtesy, and seemed rather to fear her reception of him than she his.

'After all these years,' he bowed low over her hand, 'that you should come to me is more than I ever dared hope.'

'I come,' she gained courage to tell him firmly, 'on the advice of Mr Hawkins who acts as agent for us both in this most unpleasant circumstance. I take it,' she eyed him with a cool and calculating look, 'that you are wishful to divorce me.'

He lowered his eyes from hers and was fidgeting with his sword belt. He wore his naval uniform, deliberately, she surmised, to make it the more difficult for her to speak her mind as she intended to in terms that would be the most offensive to an officer in the King's Navy. If so, he was mistaken. She gave not a fig for his uniform nor for the respect due to him as an officer who had distinguished himself on many naval occasions.

'I would not,' he said, 'desire to place you in so

compromising a position were it not that I feel it is my right to terminate a relationship that has never been more than in its legal sense a marriage since we have lived apart all these years.'

'You say it is your right – what right,' she demanded fiercely, 'have you to claim the *right* to drag me and the Duke into the mire of a divorce court on the assumption of a marriage that you admit has never been a marriage more than in its legal sense? ... No! Wait,' as he made attempt to speak. 'That which you call "marriage in its legal sense" does not exist. There has never been the consummation of a marriage save in – rape! Yes, rape!'

'I protest,' he came close to her, 'that what happened between us so many years ago –'

'When you forced an entrance into my house,' she would allow him no quarter, no brief to pursue his cause. 'You took possession of my body against my will. Can that be named in a Court of Law as anything but rape? And as for the perverted injuries I suffered on the night of what is supposed to have been a marriage, how would a Court of Law review all that I would give in evidence against you?'

She watched him pale; she had shaken him and knew she held the most formidable weapon she could use in her defence.

'You have no proof,' he began, with his lips as pale as his face, and if ever she had seen a man craven with fear she saw it now. She had drawn blood; the honour of his career as a naval officer was at stake and also it had come to her knowledge he had in mind to marry the daughter of a doctor at Bath – was it? – about twenty years younger than himself. 'No proof,' he gained voice to repeat, 'that I behaved to you in our marriage other than was a husband's privilege.'

'You liar! You –' Words spluttered from her in a volley of abusive indignation. 'You contemptible bastard! A

136

beast, lower than any beast! Do your damnedest. Go ahead with divorce proceedings and see where they will lead you – in prison for perjury and worse! – for the perverted injuries you practised against the woman you claim as wife. Go on then with your divorce and see what my lawyers will make of my defence against it. Yes, and what the Lords of the Admiralty will say against it. And what His Majesty the King will say against it because his mother knows the whole truth of the horrors I suffered from you in the name of marriage. You may remember I told you that the Dowager Princess would have had you reported to the Admiralty when, as you threatened, to acquaint Her Royal Highness of our marriage and so lose me my position at Court as Maid of Honour?'

She had him now at her mercy. He was trembling as with ague; he who had faced bombardment from enemy ships, who had fought sword to sword with the French when he and his men had stormed their battleships; he who had faced death unflinchingly for the cause of his King and country was now sunk in the face of dishonour to his name and manhood.

She had won.

Recovering his lost composure, he drew himself up to his full height and with what dignity he could muster said:

'You leave me no alternative, confronted with these false accusations, which I would not sully my rank as an officer of His Majesty's Navy to contradict.'

'You would be well advised,' said she, hotly, 'not so to attempt. I may take it then that you withdraw your suggested proceedings to sue for divorce?'

'Out of consideration for you – yes.'

'Consideration for me!' she echoed with derisive laughter. 'If that is the best possible loophole you can find to disentangle the Gordian knot you have tied to embroil yourself, then go and untie it! But you won't untie me, my *lord*,' folding back her upper lip in a sneer.

'Are you my lord yet or do I live in hope that I may be "my lady"? In which case I shall be your Countess unless –'

'Unless what?' he broke in, his pallor receding from his cheeks that looked to have sunken and in a trice hopefully expanded.

'Unless I can bring about a case that will not involve you or myself in unsavoury public litigation. How the hawks would swoop down on the carcass of a divorce and on one of us who might survive the scandal – but it won't be you, Hervey, who survives. I'll see you torn limb from limb.'

Again he had whitened, but she did not notice his fear this time. She was thinking, and presently she said:

'I believe there is a – I cannot now remember the name of it – a something by which can be proved a nullity of marriage.'

He pounced on that, and again the colour flushed back into his face. As a naval officer he had studied certain legal matters appertaining not only to the Navy and international law but also civil litigation, and was quick to seize on this.

'I presume you allude to a jactitation of marriage?'

'Yes! That is what I was thinking of a jact – er – jactick – whatever it is, meaning that a marriage can be disproved as a false pretence and that the wronged party is entitled to redress.'

'The law,' it was he who now assumed command of the situation, 'would have to decide which is the wronged party.'

'No difficulty there. I am the wronged party and if you like to go ahead with this suit as defendant, neither of us will suffer any degrading publicity because I shall instruct my attorney that it shall be heard in – what is it called? – camera.'

'It would be heard,' said he judiciously, 'in an Ecclesiastical Court.'

'Oh no!' she exclaimed, 'do you mean the Church will have to come into it?'

'Not in actuality the Church – there is no Popish dispensation in the Church of England. And I cannot but admire your – shall we say – ability in untying this very knotty Gordian knot,' was his reply with all the charm that had attracted her some twenty years ago when she had taken the 'first fool' that offered.

She held out her hand to him. Best not to be at enmity if he were as wishful as she to avoid the 'degrading publicity' of a divorce which could be less harmful to her than to her Duke.

Taking her proffered hand he raised it to his lips, turned it over and dropped a light kiss in her palm.

'We part then,' said he looking down into her eyes and thinking: she's still a damned fine woman and as lovely as ever although she must be nearer fifty than forty, 'but we part with this pledge,' he closed her hand with his kiss within it, 'as my promise that neither you nor the Duke of Kingston will suffer infamy from me in any court of law. That, I repeat, is my promise. The suit of jactitation which you and I together will devise, but never to be known that we have connived jointly in any such proceeding –'

'Which,' she withdrew her hand, 'is certain if we both want to be free.'

'You may want,' he murmured, 'but I am wondering do I.'

'You said?' For he had spoken almost below breath.

'Only that I am your servant, madam,' he bowed profoundly, 'now and for always whichever way our suit, your suit and mine, may be decided.'

He went with her to the door of his house, following behind her as if he were a lackey and, waving aside the footman, he opened the door for her and bowed again nose to knees. . . . In mockery? she wondered. And what was his intention? Fair play or foul?

Time would show.

Time did show, to the delight of Mary Coke and Walpole, from whom we may have gathered much that is entirely incorrect with perhaps one grain of truth in their voluminous letters, to damage irrevocably the name of Elizabeth Chudleigh. Yet but for these two we might have known little or nothing about this incredible young – now not so young – woman until after her death when the author of *Authentic Particulars* raked up all he could scavenge from hearsay.

However, sufficient that we can give what we do know to be a clandestine meeting between the Herveys, and admittedly to sail very near the wind of collusion; but fortunately neither Horace nor Mary Coke had an inkling that they had met, for according to Horace: 'Mr Augustus Hervey (I suppose at the desire of his brother, Lord Bristol) is going to prove his marriage as the first stage towards suing for being *un*married and has sent the lady a letter to signify his intention to which he received the answer that if he proves the marriage he will have sixteen thousand pounds to pay as she owes that sum of money ...'

We know that she no longer owed that sum of money, at least not since the ball had started to roll in the direction of the jactitation suit for a dissolution of the marriage because Kingston had paid all her debts. But Walpole, as also the industrious Mary Coke, was quick to seize on any breath of gossip to do with Elizabeth Chudleigh whom the two of them had made their chief target for so long; and now here was talk enough to keep them occupied and send them scribbling away at their desks for weeks to come.

The suit which led to a much more serious charge against Elizabeth Chudleigh than her denial of a marriage with Augustus Hervey, began more than twenty years after that disastrous 'scrambled affair of a wedding' (as she put it to Hawkins). The proceedings, which were

140

excessively dreary and long winded, were conducted before a Consistory Court in the dining-room adjoining the Common Hall of Doctors' Commons.

The judgement of the Consistory Court, to which none of the public – greatly to the chagrin of Mary Coke and Walpole – was admitted, went something in this fashion, and would have conveyed as little to any of the Mary Coke/Walpole company as it did to the parties concerned.

'In the name of God, Amen. Before you, the worshipful John Bettesworth, Doctor of Laws, Vicar General of the Right Reverend Richard by divine permission, Lord Bishop of London, constituted in this behalf of the proctor of the Honourable Elizabeth Chudleigh . . .'

Elizabeth, who had pleaded with her lawyer, William Field of the Inner Temple, to be allowed to be present at the hearing, as was also the Honourable Augustus, pricked her ears to learn from the Worshipful John Bettesworth to the effect that:

'. . . The said Honourable Elizabeth Chudleigh was in no way engaged in any matrimonial contract or espousal with the said Honourable Augustus John Hervey. That the said Augustus John Hervey did in this present year of our Lord, 1768, within the parish of St James's Westminster, and in other parishes and places in the presence of several witnesses falsely and maliciously boast and report that he was married to or contracted in marriage with the aforesaid Honourable Elizabeth Chudleigh. . . .'

She was thinking: Why does this fool keep on calling me the Honourable if I am not supposed to be the wife of the Honourable Augustus? She looked across at him where he sat at the end of the long table in the heavily mahoganied and panelled dining-room where the faces in portraits on the walls of bewigged and learned members of the law glared down at her, all of them so similar and so devoid of any significant features as to give the impression they were one and the same person. . . .

Hervey, meeting her eyes, lowered one of his eyelids in the smallest possible semblance of a wink, and she could not help but feel that now, for the first time since that tragic farce in the Chapel at Lainston they, involved in this case to their mutual advantage, were *en rapport*.

While the Worshipful John Bettesworth droned on and on she gathered that the Honourable Augustus John Hervey being asked and requested to cease, desist and abstain from the aforesaid pretended false and malicious boasting to the great danger of his soul's health – (much more danger to his soul's health, Elizabeth inwardly parenthesized, if I were to get up and tell these doctors of law how much his soul's health was endangered on our wedding night! A lot of damned ninnies). And she wondered how much money the Honourable Augustus had put in their pockets to conduct this case against him for false malicious boasting, etc. He must be as anxious, she thought, to marry that girl who ever she is as I am to marry Kingston.

... 'That Mr William Field as the attorney of Elizabeth Chudleigh' (noticeably no 'Honourable' this time) 'used to receive on her behalf her salary as Maid of Honour without the right Hon. Augustus Hervey being concerned in any way.' (Of course not, you idiot, thought she, and glancing again at Hervey he returned her another and slightly more noticeable wink) ...! And that Elizabeth Chudleigh for many years subsequent to the time of the pretended marriage has and well before and ever since the time of the pretended marriage constantly transacted business in her own name of Elizabeth Chudleigh, spinster'. ...

The Worshipful John Bettesworth having finished with the constantly false, malicious boasting etc, affirming 'with no small prejudice to the said Elizabeth Chudleigh, spinster, and she, thinking herself greatly injured, aggrieved and disquieted by reason of the aforesaid false and malicious boasting, duly complained to this Court for

142

a fit and meet remedy to be had and provided in her behalf'...

Mr William Field, the lawyer whom Elizabeth had consulted, must, she thought, have been in league with Hervey's attorney for the Worshipful John Bettesworth to have presented to the Court so formidable an indictment against the Honourable Augustus.

His defence put forward by his attorney, a Mr Fountain, was in the same incomprehensible long-winded jargon with this difference, that it presented what must have been apparent to the Worshipful John Bettesworth and all the learned and obviously bored and yawning Doctors if they had given but their attention to it, that the statements of the Honourable Augustus John Hervey were deliberately inaccurate.

The gist of his defence, as propounded by Mr Fountain, amounted to the facts that: 'The Honourable Augustus Hervey having conceived a liking and affection for the said Elizabeth Chudleigh in the year 1744 and being a bachelor and a minor of seventeen or eighteen years ...'

Lord save us! ejaculated Elizabeth to her inner self. A minor! At twenty-two. They'll have him for perjury if he don't take care.

... 'And,' imperturbably continued the wily Mr Fountain, 'being free from any matrimonial contract did privately make his addresses to the said Elizabeth Chudleigh, now Hervey –'

Why in the devil does he want to say I'm now Hervey, fumed Elizabeth, if they want to prove we were never married?

... 'And she, the said Elizabeth Chudleigh who was then also a minor of about eighteen years did receive and admit his addresses and courtship and entertain him as a suitor in the way of marriage but both being minors without the knowledge of any part of the family and servants of the said Mr Merrill deceased in whose house the couple resided'...

Evidently the Consistorial Episcopal Court was ready to accept that: 'The right Honourable Augustus John Hervey, bachelor, calling himself the husband of the Honourable Elizabeth Chudleigh, hath totally failed in the proof of his allegation whereby he pleaded and propounded a pretended marriage to have been solemnized between him and the said Elizabeth Chudleigh, spinster . . . and that he was *not* contracted in marriage to the said Elizabeth Chudleigh'. . .

'I have this to say,' and to Caesar Hawkins did she say it when after the Court had decided in her favour and awarded her costs of a hundred pounds to be paid by the Honourable Augustus, 'that Hervey shows up very well in the whole of this, to me, entirely incomprehensible business. The case against him and for me seems to be decided on those lies he told about our ages. We were not minors as you know.'

Hawkins gave her a twinkling look.

'It is worth a hundred pounds to Hervey to deduct a few years off both your ages, and to allow himself to be accused of falsely and maliciously boasting and all the rest of it that he had married you. Whether he did or did not marry you is no concern of mine, but the main thing is you both wanted to be quit of each other, he to marry a young lady at the Bath –'

'Is there,' she interrupted, 'really such a young lady? Or does he just want to be free of what has never been a marriage except in name?' She wondered if Hervey would ever want to marry any woman, aware – as Hawkins was not – of the predilections of the Honourable Augustus.

'There is a young person, a Miss Moysey, I understand, to whom he has been showing unmistakable attention.'

'I pity her if she takes him! But as it were better I do not tell him myself, would you,' asked Elizabeth, 'please convey to him from me that he need not pay me one penny piece of that hundred pounds costs. I'll pay them to him or to his lawyer myself in gratitude for the lies he told to untie the Gordian Knot. He will know what you mean by that . . . By the way, you didn't – did you' – the face upraised to his showed sudden swift alarm – 'tell him you knew I had or did have a son?'

'Is it likely?' replied Hawkins. His grizzled grey eyebrows jutting above his professionally shrewd eyes rose to the lines on his forehead under the cumbersome wig with the remark:

'I presumed that Hervey was your husband, but as subsequent events in the Ecclesiastical Court have proved that the marriage was not – ah – valid, that is to say not consummated, it is immaterial to me who was the father of your child.'

'I know,' she said, and faint amusement dawned as she answered him, 'that you as Court Surgeon do not concern yourself with the parentage of the babies you deliver to the unmarried Maids of Honour. Your medical attention to me and all of us is strictly confidential.'

'Certainly, madam, unless the father of the child has called me to attend to the birth of an infant born to him.'

'I am eternally grateful to you, Mr Hawkins, for your advice and assistance in securing me my freedom from what has never been a marriage and so –'

'And so,' he concluded for her, 'may I be the first to congratulate you on your betrothal to the Duke of Kingston?'

'That,' said she, 'will be strictly private as will also be our wedding, if it should ever take place.'

'I quite understand, madam,' he replied, who did not at all understand; for if her marriage to the Duke of Kingston should never take place why had she gone to such lengths to obtain an annulment of her marriage to the future Earl of Bristol? He had summed her up accurately enough to realize that her one ambition was aggrandizement. If that were her only fault, or weakness, it was shared by a dozen others of her kind. A childish desire for the best that life could offer of material comfort and luxury. She wanted, as a child might want, extravagant playthings, in her case to have the power due to the wife of a Duke or an Earl with ample means to gratify her pleasures, her grand parties, her army of servants, her coaches, her beautiful homes. . . . All these, mused the surgeon as he went his way after leaving her in the house at Knightsbridge, are just the amplified cravings of the adolescent which she still is mentally. Although a woman of intelligence she is strangely divided. It is as if her personality were split in two. No harm in that. I have met it before in some of our most notable politicians, or in the young King himself. . . .

Little did the learned medico-surgeon realize that he was anticipating the psychological reasoning of two hundred years later, not that his idea of a split personality approached the psychiatric diagnosis of the twentieth-century schizoid. The idea, indeed the very words, were as unknown to his medical research as Hindustani, and it is certain he entertained no such connection with the Chudleigh's *folie de grandeur*. Half the women who married into the peerage could be, he decided, guilty of the same and not unnatural ambition. His own wife was for ever pestering him as to why he did not approach the Prime Minister or the Princess Dowager, who regarded him with much esteem, to bestow upon him the honour of, if not a peerage, a baronetcy . . . His meditations were halted by his name called from behind him. He had chosen to dismiss his carriage and walk to his house in Duke Street, St James's.

Wheeling round he saw that Hervey had hailed him.

'Well, sir, I have you to thank,' was the greeting of the Hon. Augustus, 'for landing me into a hundred pounds costs.'

'You are mistaken, sir.' Hawkins eyed him with the utmost disfavour. 'I am commissioned on behalf of Mistress Chudleigh to convey to you her decision to pay the costs awarded to her as damages for what has been proven to be a falsifying of the alleged marriage between you and this much injured lady.'

'Much injured be damned!' he let forth, his face suffused with reddening indignation. 'Any injury suffered is on my account, not hers. I stood up there in my defence by perjuring myself as to my age and hers as minors – actually I was a minor being but twenty years old – and if those damned fools conducting the case had taken the trouble to investigate the marriage certificate which is still in existence as I happen to know, I was laying myself open to a criminal offence. Perjury, damme!'

'To say nothing,' said Hawkins with elaborate suavity, 'of mutual collusion.'

Hervey grinned a trifle crookedly.

'To which you were, as her adviser, a party?'

'Not at all. She asked my advice in this most difficult and unpleasant case, and I advised her to approach you, sir, and come to some agreement as to whether a divorce, which she, understandably, was reluctant to agree, were possible. There being no evidence whatsoever of your – or Mistress Chudleigh – having committed adultery, since there was and never had been a marriage between you.'

'You have it all tied up, haven't you?'

'There was some mention,' Hawkins shifted his gaze from that of the Hon. Augustus, 'of untying a Gordian knot when the lady instructed me to let you know that her wish to pay your costs is in gratitude for the – ah – the lies you told in court to insure her freedom.'

'It was her wish to be free,' retorted Hervey. 'Had I my way I'd have claimed her as my wife. Do you think I'd have gone through all that murky business just to allow her to be the Duchess of Kingston?'

'I am given to understand,' Hawkins was now gazing at a point above Hervey's shoulder, 'that you are desirous of marrying again, and that your choice is for a young lady residing at the Bath.'

'Goddamme!' exploded Hervey. 'Is there nothing that these bloody sods don't know or guess at, who have naught to do but gather up the garbage scattered by the Court and that scandal-monger Walpole! He's the one who has set the ball rolling!'

So saying, Hervey turned on his heel and left Hawkins to go his own way home, no wiser if Elizabeth's offer to pay Hervey's costs for damages awarded had been accepted or not. If not, he decided, Hervey can pay them and let us hope this is the end of it all.

Hervey was not mistaken as to the origin of the rumour that he intended to marry again, for we have Walpole relating his version of the case brought before the Ecclesiastical Court: 'That the fair Chudleigh appeared in Doctors' Commons and swore by the Virgin Mary and Diana that she never was married to Mr Hervey!' We know that the 'fair Chudleigh' did not appear in court, at least not in evidence, but was represented by her attorney who did all the swearing. Yet Walpole has it that 'the fair injured innocence who is fifty' (she was not fifty but Walpole added three or more years to her) 'is to be married to the Duke of Kingston who has kept her openly for almost half that time' . . . He even goes on to describe that her wedding gown will be of 'White satin, trimmed with Brussels lace and pearls. Every word of this history', he maintains, 'is true'.

He then gives us news of the physician whose daughter Horace names with chuckles as 'Miss Rhubarb', evidently having been unable to find any other name for her. 'The physician,' he tells us, 'who is little more in his senses than the other actors and a little honester' (certainly more honest than our Horace!), 'has offered his daughter five thousand pounds not to marry Mr Hervey; but Miss Rhubarb persists, though there is no more doubt of the marriage of Mr Hervey and Miss Chudleigh than that of your father and mother. . . .'

This letter ends with the ambiguous opinion that: 'It is

a cruel case upon his family who can never acquiesce in the legitimacy of his children if any come from this bigamy. . . .'

The first allusion to what would be the ultimate result of the judgement of Doctors' Commons in that famous jactitation case.

SEVEN

It was now the talk of the Town that the Chudleigh was to marry the Duke of Kingston. In London drawing-rooms the news of it was led by Lady Mary Coke, with her intimates gathered round her all ears for the latest information, who tells as she wrote in her diary:

'She, the Chudleigh, has taken an oath that she is *not* Hervey's wife, but everybody knows she is. Yet since all the witnesses to the marriage are dead she thinks she's safe to remarry.'

'But surely,' this from the Duchess of Newcastle, who had no liking for the Chudleigh since her husband, the Duke, had been another of Elizabeth's numerous admirers, 'surely Kingston couldn't think of marrying her when he knows she is Hervey's wife?'

'It has been proved – if proof can be bribed,' said Mary Coke, 'that there was no marriage. At least, none which could be recognized, as both were minors – they *say* – and the parents of neither had given their consent. Thus is vice encouraged that I'm persuaded she will be visited by half the *ton* so soon as she is Duchess of Kingston.'

'Did you say bribed?' Another of the ladies agog for this most interesting side-light on the all-absorbing topic. 'If so, then it must have cost them a mint, besides committing perjury. Minors indeed! They were both in their twenties.'

'I understand that Hervey was as unwilling to bring witnesses to prove the marriage as was the Chudleigh, both determined to remarry. But I think Hervey's choice will not come up to his expectations. The girl's father has something to say about that. In any case,' Lady Mary reluctantly was forced to admit, 'the Chudleigh will soon be the Duchess of Kingston. Although,' and this rejoiced her listeners to hear, 'I understand the Archbishop has refused to grant a licence for Kingston to marry her.'

'Then they can't get married!' hopefully declared the Duchess of Newcastle.

But they could and they did get married with the Archbishop's licence granted when applied for. And the marriage was duly and truly solemnized and registered in the Church of St Margaret's, Westminster, in March 1769 between:

The Most Honourable Evelyn Pierrepoint, Duke of Kingston, and the Honourable Elizabeth Chudleigh of Knightsbridge married by special licence of the Archbishop of Canterbury the 8th day of March 1769, by me
Samuel Harpur

in the presence of:

There are nine witnesses, headed by Lord Masham, in waiting on the King. Masham had asked leave of His Majesty to attend the wedding of the Duke of Kingston that he might give Mistress Chudleigh away.

Great was the disappointment – no! the infuriation – of Lady Mary on learning that the Archbishop had not refused the licence.

But there was one more than Mary Coke, more than that arch-gossip Walpole, who had reason to resent the triumph of Elizabeth Chudleigh in achieving the height of her ambition. This was Whitehead, who went far to bring about her downfall, prompted by the thirst for revenge upon the wife – if wife she were – of his master, the Duke, whom he had served for many years. He was not disposed to be dismissed his service at the Duke's house in Arlington Street where he had reigned supreme in the servants' hall and be lodged at Kingston House in Knightsbridge, renamed by the newly made Duchess, and to be under the control of an autocratic mistress instead of an easy-going master.

Fortunately for Elizabeth she did not know, when taking over the management of her husband's households as was her right as his wife, that she had made a life-long enemy of the valet Whitehead, who was compiling a series of letters, published many years later, in which he drew grossly exaggerated and defamatory details of the domestic life of his master and mistress, deliberately aimed to injure the Duchess.

From the very first Whitehead made no secret of his resentment against the control of the newly made Duchess who took complete command of her husband and his servants. Why not? When she discovered how the Duke had been rooked by his staff and not the least of them Whitehead who had systematically feathered his nest at the Duke's expense for years. The careless, good-natured Evelyn Pierrepoint had never questioned his valet's stewardship of tradesmen's accounts nor the wages of the staff paid twice over. But not now that the 'Duchess' (Whitehead never alluded to her title without a sneer) had taken control in the running of all domestic affairs, no longer the Duke's 'kept woman', as Whitehead would refer to her among his fellow servants, but Whitehead's mistress and the Duke's wife to give him orders and look into every account rendered by the tradesmen which she and not Whitehead would pay.

Not only to Whitehead was Elizabeth's marriage to Kingston bitter gall. As the Duke's mistress, the ladies of the Court had accepted her hospitality as nominal hostess to Kingston, and knew that his lavish entertainments at her request were indulgently paid by him. But now that she was in truth his wife and Duchess, she could and did take precedence over many of them, besides remaining the Princess Dowager's favourite, not now her Maid of Honour but her closest and most intimate friend.

The Dowager, poor soul, who had undergone as much malicious spiteful gossip as Elizabeth had endured for all these years, was in sore need of friendship from the one loyal woman about her who could contradict and defend the scandalous talk and blasts of ribaldry in broadsides directed at a 'wanton widow and her Scottish paramour', whom the enemies of Bute spread about their names as 'the rulers of Britain'.

Yet with the same disdainful indifference to slander with which Elizabeth had ignored the calumnies directed at her, so did the King's mother defy the bombardment of insults volleyed at her and her 'goot Bute' in broadsides of the crudest ribaldry hawked about the streets and at the very gates of Leicester House.

But there were worse worries for the Dowager Princess to confide in her 'Goot Duchess'. (What satisfaction it must have been to Elizabeth to be no longer the 'goot Miss Chudleigh' or, on rare occasions, the 'goot Elizabet'.) Apart from the knowledge of that which even her 'goot Duchess' was unaware, the King's mother was dying. The Princess had been of late more pale, frequently so tired that she had to take to bed in the daytime, yet on the occasions when Elizabeth visited the Dowager, she appeared to be well enough; worried, yes, and anxious, but not, to Elizabeth's knowledge, ill. That the Princess bore with heroic fortitude the pangs of the dread disease that was eating away her life, forbidding her doctors to tell her son, the King, of her condition, should have moderated the vile accusations levelled at her for her association with Lord Bute, had those who decried her known of it. But only too late did they know of it. She was libelled and insulted to the end of her life.

Yet while Elizabeth fought violently on her mistress's behalf if, in her hearing, those should slur the name of the Dowager Princess with the breath of their noisome innuendoes, she could not stop their tongues any more than she could stop the venom they spat at herself.

It was on one of her twice or thrice monthly visits to Her Royal Highness that Elizabeth heard of a most disturbing family event which soon became the greatest of all scandals to delight the gossip-mongers, greater than anything to do with 'the Chudleigh' or the Dowager Princess.

At the death of the King's uncle, the Duke of Cumberland, his title passed to the King's youngest brother, Henry Frederick. He was a stupid, rakish, lecherous young fool and had been described as 'rushing from the schoolroom to the stews'. Had he confined himself solely to 'the stews' he might not have fallen into the appalling situation in which he became embroiled. But he fell in love with Lady Grosvenor, an equally rakish young woman, easily seducible and of exceeding beauty. The amorous Duke was an instant victim to her sirenic allure. To the horror of his brother, the King, and his mother, the Dowager Princess, he was cited with a charge of adultery and tried in public by the husband of Lady Grosvenor for damages!

'*Du lieber Gott!*' moaned the Dowager to the ever sympathetic Elizabeth, 'such letters that haf been read in court – the whole of London has know of them. Vat disgrace to the King and to me – a Prince of the Bloodt Royal.'

The letters from the King's brother read to the court convulsed the public, who avidly listened from the gallery. They were couched in the most ardent if misspelt but none the less sincere declarations to the 'dearest Angel of his Soul. . . . I prayed for you, my dearest love, I kissed your dear little hairs and lay down and dreamt of you and had you on your dear little couch ten thousand times. . . .'

The result of these effusions that caused the King a brainstorm and the King's mother a fit, from which she was in no condition to recover without more serious effect to her failing health, was the award of ten thousand pounds damages to Lord Grosvenor.

In the clubs of St James's the blades, or macaronies (the latest designation of the young sparks who had nothing to do but to drink and wench and delight in the doings of the King's foolhardy brother), the letter was discussed *ad nauseam*. 'The most expensive dream on record!' declared one of them, a trifle envious maybe that he had not been cited by the Earl of Grosvenor, whose lady had probably also been had by him on her dear little couch ten thousand times. Nor was this the last of the humiliating business to the Royal Family.

Elizabeth, then at Thoresby, the Duke's Nottingham-shire seat, when the Cumberland–Grosvenor case had partially subsided, was able to impart to her 'Evie' something of more disastrous trouble than the amorous indiscretions of the King's brother, Henry.

Elizabeth greatly enjoyed her visits to Thoresby where she was now the mistress of her Duke's household. Hitherto she had paid *sub rosa* visits to this, his chief and most important country seat. But now, to the festering rancour of Whitehead, she was mistress not only of Thoresby but of all the Duke's houses and all his men and maidservants. Whitehead had much to tell in his letters published when Elizabeth was no longer alive to deny his allegations that, contrary to the Duke, described by Whitehead as 'mild, generous, unassuming and modest in the extreme', the Duchess, as Whitehead venomously has it, was 'presumptuous, vain, imperious, meanly avaricious and cunning, a dupe to grossest flattery. . . . Connected with such a woman,' continues this sententious scribe, 'it cannot be supposed that the Duke of Kingston could enjoy connubial happiness.'

That the newly married pair did enjoy 'connubial happiness' must have greatly exacerbated Whitehead. For when at Thoresby Elizabeth much preferred that they should lead a quiet country life, 'Like any old middle-aged couple', she said. 'I just want to forget all about the spite and jealousies and jostlings for favour that goes on at the Court – or rather used to go on at the Court, but not now with the Queen and her litters.'

'Litters!' the Duke roared with laughter. She never

failed to amuse him. 'That's just what they are – her perennial litters! 'Tis all very different at Buckingham House than it was at St James's in my day.'

'And in mine.' They were walking beside the lake at Thoresby. The Duke had been out fishing all the morning, and looked tired. Elizabeth had noted that of late he tired easily, and she was for ever on the watch for symptoms that caused her some anxiety which she reported to Hawkins.

'He seems to be inclined to breathlessness after any undue exertion, and he is taking rather more than he used to drink of late.'

Hawkins reassured her.

'His Grace is no longer so young as he was, and good wine in moderation cannot cause him any ill effect. A day's fishing is the best possible relaxation he can take. You have no need to be anxious about your husband's health.'

But on this November afternoon as they walked beside the lake she was a little anxious; her Evie had about his lips a somewhat blue tinge, and yet his face, always ruddy, seemed to glow with added colour. He had stoutened, and although they walked slowly he was puffing and blowing far too much. 'Let us sit here,' she indicated a rustic seat facing the lake. 'I am rather tired.'

She mustn't let him think she had observed that *he* was tired. He would never admit he was not always in the pink of condition.

The sun, red as a holly berry, sank leisurely behind the distant hills, but the day had been warmer than the time of the year warranted, and a lilac mist enwrapped the higher slopes of the fringed hills, closely wooded; the hills of Sherwood Forest.

She was telling him:

'I am worried about the Dowager Princess. She is in a continuous state of anxiety over the latest adventure of the Duke of Cumberland.'

The Duke, gazing upward at the flight of a pheasant said:

'The coverts are full of them. That's a fine young cock. We must have another shoot next week and bring 'em down. . . . You were saying?'

'Henry of Cumberland has been off with the old love, who cost him ten thousand pounds, and is on with the new love. He has married her.'

'Who,' asked the Duke vaguely, his mind on cock pheasants, 'has married whom?'

'Henry Cumberland, the King's brother, has married Anne Horton, Lord Irnham's daughter – she's a widow, very young and beautiful. They went to Calais on a pre-marital honeymoon and Henry then wrote from an hotel where they were staying to tell the King he was married.'

'Well, why not? Better than being dragged through the divorce court to marry the Grosvenor girl.'

'*She* isn't a girl, but this one is, and Henry Cumberland doesn't appear to be the first who has enlivened her widowhood, though the first to be her second husband.'

'Why should this put the Dowager Princess into a state? After all, they are married.'

'That's just it. She's a commoner. The Princess says the King is beside himself. Short of divorce, she told me, which is unthinkable, nothing could be done to untie the marriage which has been solemnized in Holy Church. The Royal brothers cannot marry without the King's consent and then only to a Princess of the Blood.'

'Judging by the Princesses of the Blood that I have seen,' said Kingston with a throaty chuckle, 'the King's brothers would be better married without the King's consent to another Anne Horton or –' he took her hand and held it to his chest – 'or to you were you not mine. Wonder 'tis the King or his brothers didn't make a set at you.'

'My dear life!' she threw her head back laughing – she had a husky provocative laugh, one of her numerous attractions. 'The King was at least fifteen years younger than I when I saved him from the Quakeress Hannah Lightfoot, and his brothers were younger still. I've never aspired to Royalty.'

'Yet Royalty aspired to you,' the Duke remarked with a sidelong glance. 'I remember how the late King made unmistakable advances to you. It is all to your credit – and my good luck – that you didn't respond.'

'Why good luck to you that I refused that old rip's advances?'

'Because I knew you to be all that I asked for in a wife – as you are now – unpossessed by any other than myself.'

'Not even Hervey? You are right.' She could say that with confidence for while the Duke had known her for no virgin when they first were lovers, she had told him all since she became his mistress, of the horrors she had suffered on her wedding night and of the subsequent forcible intercourse that had given her Hervey's son. That she had kept nothing from Kingston went far to cement his love for and complete faith in her.

'She has him under her petticoats as well as under her thumb,' was Whitehead's incessant grumble. That he knew nothing of the disastrous marriage, more than the jactitation suit which had declared it null and void, was fortunate for Elizabeth since Whitehead's burning desire that had become an obsession, was to bring about a breach between the Duke and the Duke's wife.

Elizabeth realized his enmity was prompted by his fear that he would no longer have control of the Duke's purse nor of the Duke and that any day might bring about his dismissal, which eventually it did. But not yet. Elizabeth was not ready to shoot her bolt at the perfidious Whitehead. She knew the Duke valued his service and she also knew that Whitehead was in her power; she had only to wait her opportunity to have him out. That opportunity would not be long in coming. Meanwhile Elizabeth had more to concern her than the problems of her servants, of whom she intended to make a clean sweep when the time should be ripe.

Watching the sky aflame with the crimson sun's cremation, she rose from the seat and with her arm through the Duke's they walked back to the house. The slow death-fall of autumn leaves scattered their path like newly minted pennies.

'The gardeners should have cleared these leaves,' she said; and added, 'Your late butler, Phillips, whom I provided with a situation – you remember this, don't you?'

The Duke nodded; he remembered nothing of 'this' for since their marriage, he had left everything to his wife to manage his household's affairs.

'Well, if you remember, which you evidently don't, I arranged that he should be given the post of steward to Holme Pierrepoint' (another of Kingston's estates), 'but I found it necessary to have him dismissed. He was screwing the tenants unmercifully – he used to take their hay and poultry without paying them a penny for what he literally stole from them. He took a poor woman's sow with a young farrow of piglets and sent them to Nottingham market to be sold and never gave her any of the money they fetched. It is deplorable the way your servants have taken advantage of your generosity and indulgence. It was a great mistake on my part to have offered Phillips the situation, but I had regard for his wife – she was a Mrs Amis, the widow of a clergyman at Lainston where I used to visit my Aunt Hanmer. And I introduced her to Phillips in the first place.'

It was not thought derogatory for the widow of a clergyman of an impoverished parish to marry a butler, since the superior servants in a ducal household were considered to be on an equal social footing with an undistinguished parish priest. 'You see,' she squeezed his arm closer to her side, 'I find almost your entire staff to have no interest in you more than what they can pick from your pocket. Whitehead, for instance –'

This was the first time she had ever hinted at her determination to be even with Whitehead for his scarcely veiled insolence and for undermining her position with the remainder of the staff; also she knew that if he could he would cause a breach between her and the Duke. But he could not. She was secure if Whitehead were not.

'What of Whitehead?' Kingston turned his head sharply. 'Have you any reason to doubt his loyalty to me?'

'Not his loyalty to you, my love, but because he has been so long in your service as your confidential man-servant, he resents the intrusion of a woman into your – and his – bachelor establishment.'

'If he has been of any annoyance to you, my darling, I shall take him to task.'

'No, don't for goodness sake! These devoted men-servants can make a mort of trouble where the mistress of a house has the right to take command, when before she was merely the mistress of his master.'

'That,' said Kingston glumly, 'was never my desire as you know. Had I my way you would have been my wife these twenty years.'

'Not twenty, dearest, exactly seventeen years since we first met.'

'Ah, yes, but I sighted you at Vauxhall a year before that and determined there and then that she and only she would be my wife.'

'Not ever,' said she slyly, 'although you were attached to Madame la Touche?'

'Not attached – *de*tached from the moment I set eyes on you.'

Which was all very gratifying, and would have caused Whitehead more vexation to brood upon had he overheard it.

'Oh, look!' Elizabeth was staring ahead of her, 'is not that Lord Byron* on the terrace?'

* Lord Byron, the fifth peer and great-uncle of the poet.

'Byron?' exclaimed Kingston. 'So it is,' shortsightedly applying a quizzing glass to his eye. ''Pon my soul! The fellow has the impudence of the devil to come here after what he did to my deer with his infernal staghounds!'

What Lord Byron did with his 'infernal' staghounds had happened some few months before. Byron, who kept the King's hounds, would hunt the Duke's deer from the Forest of Sherwood on Byron's estate into Thoresby Park, and on one occasion had driven a terrified red deer into the Duke's lake. There had been in consequence an unarmed feud between the two landowners, and Kingston forbade his keepers and his huntsmen to permit Lord Byron ever to be seen on Thoresby land, at his lordship's peril.

'Who,' demanded Kingston, in red-hot rage, 'has dared let the fellow in here and on my terrace?'

'Calm yourself, love,' she soothed him, alarmed at his heightened colour and the veins, as she had described them to Hawkins, 'like ridges standing out on his forehead'. 'He may not have come for any trespassing purpose but to see you about some matter of business.'

'I'll see him in hell first,' muttered Kingston, but as always he allowed his wife to take command.

Byron, perceiving their approach, came forward to meet them and said, profusely bowing to the lady:

'I trust your Grace will forgive this intrusion, but unfortunately one of my hounds has got out of the kennels and driven another of your deer into the lake.'

'Good God!' cried Kingston, 'not *again*! I can have you prosecuted for this – and I will!'

'I pray you, Kingston,' Byron had all to lose from Kingston's hostility, having but a few years before escaped execution for the murder of Kingston's greatest friend and neighbour, Chaworth of Annesley, 'bear with me. I have dismissed my huntsman, or rather the fellow responsible for letting the hound lose, but as all attempts to rescue the stag struggling in the lake –'

'We have just come from the lake,' interrupted the Duke, 'and I saw no stag there.'

'It is at the far end of the lake bordering the forest,' explained Byron. 'You would not have seen what had occurred. I have come to beg you to lend me one of your boats that I may rescue the deer who baffles all attempts to save him.'

'No boat of mine,' retorted the incensed Kingston, 'shall be sent to the rescue of my stag that your hound has driven into the lake, as once before, to drown him. And as your hound has driven him in he can drive him out.'

'No, Evie,' Elizabeth intervened. 'You can't let the stag drown.' Then as she saw Whitehead approach, silent-footed as usual, for he would always manifest himself as if he appeared from thin air keeping eyes and ears wide open for any contact between his Grace and his Grace's 'woman' that might be to her disadvantage: 'Whitehead,' she ordered him, 'send one of the boatmen to rescue the stag that his lordship's hound has driven into the lake.'

Whitehead hesitated, eyeing her with his customary undisguised disdain and ignoring her order:

'Is it your Grace's wish,' he addressed his master, 'that the stag shall be saved from his lordship's hound or shall I have the hound destroyed?'

'Do not dare,' cried Elizabeth in a white fury, 'to question my command. Order a boatman to rescue the deer at once or you will be instantly dismissed.'

Whitehead bowed, not to her, to the Duke, and turned towards the nearest boathouse. It was as well for Elizabeth that she did not see the look of envenomed hate that distorted Whitehead's face, nor hear his mutter: 'One more nail in your coffin, your *Dis*grace!'

'I cannot sufficiently thank your Grace for your clemency,' said Byron, bowing to the Duchess; a stout, burly, heavily jowled fellow was he with no sign of the beauty that would distinguish his immortal descendant.

'Get out of my domain!' shouted Kingston. 'What my wife has had the clemency to allow you has none of my approval.'

An unfortunate incident in so far as it concerned Elizabeth since it caused even deeper enmity against her from Whitehead as she would learn to her cost.

As for the source of Kingston's hostility to Byron, the hounding of his deer was but a secondary offence to the death of his friend Chaworth, a cousin of Lord Byron. These two were never on the best of terms because Chaworth had dealt sternly with poachers on his domain which Byron ignored, declaring the best way to preserve game was to pay no heed to it, thereby admitting he was on the side of the poachers, his own tenants who had been caught snaring Chaworth's game.

The result of all this was a violent quarrel between Byron and Chaworth that ended in tragedy with Byron stabbing Chaworth to death. Accused of murder Byron, tried by his peers, was eventually acquitted. But the stigma stuck. He was known as 'The Wicked Baron' to his dying day and Kingston never forgave him for the death of his friend.

Whitehead, following their Graces at a distance as they took their homeward way, was not slow to realize that, for once, the Duke had been seriously annoyed with his wife.

Having seen them in their sanctum, a charming room decorated by Elizabeth with starry blossomed curtains, a less pretentious and more homely room than the elaborate suites of apartments where they would entertain, Whitehead made sure that no footman nor any servants were within sight or sound before he knelt to put his ear to the keyhole and delightedly heard:

'My love, I have allowed you every indulgence in the management of my household and servants, but that you should have countermanded my orders regarding Byron's demand for a boat to rescue the stag his hound had driven – not for the first time – into the lake is really exceeding my – your privilege.'

'*My* privilege!'

Whitehead gleefully rubbed his hands together. She was evidently about to let forth in one of her abusive tempers, which Whitehead had often overheard and grossly exaggerated as 'the language of a fish fag' . . . 'Have I not the privilege to save you from the vengeful malice of a man whose name stinks throughout the country?'

'But not to countermand my orders to Whitehead, my personal servant who has been in my employ all these years. You may order your own servants do this, do that, without interference from me.'

'As so I should think! As for your Whitehead – I tell you he has been systematically robbing you all these years of what he calls his perquisites. I know for a fact that he searches your pockets after you have gone to bed and takes out what money is there and your letters, which he reads.'

'The devilish bitch!' muttered Whitehead, clenching and unclenching his fists as if he would have had his hands upon the lady's throat.

'I know that Whitehead goes through my clothes,' he heard the Duke say, 'but he always gives me back the money he finds in my pockets because he fears someone might come and rifle what was in them if he did not take charge of –'

'You poor fool!' She would not let Kingston finish this mild extenuation of his favourite and devoted Whitehead's methods. 'Can't you see how you've been diddled by all of them? You must get Whitehead out – get *all* of them out and I'll engage an entirely new staff. I was able to rid you of your butler Phillips who married Mrs Amis, the wife of the incumbent of Lainston. I arranged that, and you remember what I discovered about *him*? I now advise – no, I insist that you rid yourself of Whitehead, whom you've pampered and trusted, and whose insolence and resentment against me, your wife, I will no longer tolerate. Either he goes or I go!'

'It will be you,' muttered Whitehead removing his ear from the keyhole, his face distorted with rage, '*you* who will go, if not now at some later time when I've done with you, and *for* you, my lady. . . .'

But the very next day he was told by the Duke:

'Whitehead, we must part. I have been informed of what has gone on too long in my house unknown to me.'

Standing very straight Whitehead took what he had expected to hear, his face turned a sickly yellow although his answer was as ever humbly servile.

'Your Grace must know I would never see you robbed nor wronged, but as it is evident that now her Grace is mistress of your household as' (with obsequious head bowing), 'it is her Grace's right to order her household and your Grace's servants, I take my notice and rely on your Grace's goodwill to one who has served you faithfully with all my heart.'

He manufactured as near a sob in his voice as would convince the unsuspicious, gullible Kingston of the man's loyalty, and made him reconsider what seemed to be too harsh a judgement on one who had 'served him faithfully with all his heart'. And again the next day the Duke sent him word that he retracted the notice he had given him and that he could remain in the service of his Grace until some future date, depending upon how he performed his duties in obedience to his Grace's command.

This message, dictated by Elizabeth, who had seen the Duke was taking it hardly that he had been persuaded to dismiss Whitehead at her instigation, was delivered by Kingston's agent, Colonel Litchfield; and there the matter was allowed to stay in temporary abeyance. Yet Whitehead knew he was foredoomed.

He had been prepared for that and was taking every

possible means to have 'done with and *for* his lady' as he had promised himself and her.

So much for Thomas Whitehead, who persistently preserved his injured innocence and his faithful devoted service to his master, while he plotted to be revenged for his dismissal that he knew was bound to be brought about by 'a wicked designing woman', she who had beguiled the Duke into a marriage for which Whitehead would leave no stone unturned to prove was *no* marriage! He had carefully followed the jactitation suit and had it firmly fixed in his mind there had been collusion between the Herveys, who were legally man and wife, although the Episcopal court had found the marriage null and void.

His first step towards that which he determined would be Her *Dis*grace's downfall was to get in touch with Mrs Judith Phillips, once the wife of the Rev. Thomas Amis, deceased, and now married to the discharged Duke's butler, Phillips.

That Mrs Phillips was beholden to the Duchess when as 'Miss Chudleigh' she had secured the post of butler for her husband, had placed her under an obligation to Elizabeth. Whitehead had discovered that Mrs Amis before her marriage to Phillips had visited Miss Chudleigh at the Duke's house in Arlington Street and also at Kingston House.

Having ascertained that Mrs Phillips was living in London and found out exactly where, he lost no time in communicating with her 'on a matter that concerned her welfare and that of her husband'.

This letter resulted in a meeting between Mrs Phillips and Whitehead at Arlington Street on one of the few occasions when the Kingstons were in London from Thoresby. The interview took place in Whitehead's own sanctum appropriated by himself when in attendance on the Duke at one or other of his London houses.

166

Over liberal supplies of madeira wine and pleasantries exchanged, Whitehead informed Mrs Phillips how it had come to his knowledge that her late husband, the Rev. Mr Amis, had performed the marriage ceremony between the Hon. Augustus Hervey and Miss Chudleigh.

'I am bound to tell you, my dear Mrs Phillips,' Whitehead replenished the lady's glass, 'that there may be further investigations into the marriage of his Grace, the Duke of Kingston, with the – ah – the lady who is presumably his wife. You may have heard that the suit conducted by the Ecclesiastical Court two or three years ago found the marriage ceremony performed by your late husband was no marriage at all. The Court decided in favour of the – ah – the woman who now claims to be his Grace's Duchess, but I understand that you held the certificate of marriage when Mr Merrill, who is now dead, had been given the certificate into his charge and handed it over to you.'

'Yes, he did.' Mrs Phillips, rodent-faced with projecting teeth and timid hare's eyes, took another draught of madeira and was emboldened thereby to say:

'I never wanted to have anything to do with it. But Mr Merrill persuaded me, in case anything should happen to him, that I should keep the certificate. It was all so very hurried and done at dead of night – I mean the wedding. And she, the Duchess as she is now –'

'As she may not be now,' said Whitehead smoothly, 'in view of certain information that has arisen concerning the marriage of his Grace to the – to Mrs Hervey.'

'Oh dear!' Mrs Phillips set down her glass to clasp her hands, 'I don't know where it is –'

'Where what is?' Whitehead again refilled her empty glass, noting that the eyes of Mrs Phillips were assuming more than ever the look, a trifle glazed, of a trapped hare. 'Pray do not alarm yourself, madam, I have no wish to give you any needless anxiety on the question of Mrs – ah – Mrs Hervey's marriage, but merely to ask that you will be able to produce the certificate of the marriage if called upon to do so.'

'Oh dear, oh dear!' Mrs Phillips distractedly repeated. 'I don't know, I'm sure. I had forgotten all about it. I remember – Oh, thank you, I think I've had enough – an excellent ver – ver – vintage but I am unused to – Well, if you inshis – insist.'

'When the late Mr Merrill asked you to take charge of the certificate, pray allow me – yes, I do insist – am I correct in assuming that he made a copy of it to give to the incumbent of Lainston parish church?'

'I – I don't remember. I think he had a copy or it may have been the – the book.'

'The book?' encouraged Whitehead.

'There was a – Mr Spears – er – Spearing, yes, he was the att – the att'ney who brought the book – my husband signed it. It –' Mrs Phillips was now becoming somewhat incoherent – 'it is sho – sho long 'go.'

'Quite so. But you have met with Mrs Hervey – or Miss Chudleigh as then she called herself – since her marriage to the Duke?'

'No, not shince her marriage – she invited me to Kingshton House and I 'member,' Mrs Phillips was now in the giggles, 'that she – tee-hee – she shaid she could have been married twice an' now I'm – no, *she* shaid – I'm an ol' maid! Me I thought t'was a funny thing to say when she was living at the Duke's house or with the Duke as't might be an' being married to Mr Hervey as was married by my husband so I couldna' help but laugh.' Nor could Mrs Phillips help but laugh again until she toppled sideways from the table and was caught by Whitehead just in time before she fell.

So they were both laughing, Whitehead well pleased with his success in gaining even this much confirmation of his suspicions, having already ascertained quite enough for him to formulate his plans when opportunity should arise.

Finding Mrs Phillips to be so easily persuaded under the influence of his Grace's choicest madeira to fall in if not to fall under the table with his tentative suggestions, he then proceeded further to encoil Mrs Phillips in his attempt to damnify her Disgraceful Grace.

'Too cruel,' he murmured as once more and for the last time he refilled the glass of Mrs Phillips, seeing she was so far gone that she might not be sufficiently conscious to take in his final and most deadly objective. 'Cruel indeed that the mackin –,' he too had some slight difficulty in this pronunciation, 'as I was saying –' and very clearly and deliberately he said it '– mack-in-nations' (the Duke's madeira was a decidedly excellent vintage), 'of the lady who calls herself the Duchess of Kingston should 'ave been the means of your good husband's end.'

'His – his – end? Phil'ps end? How does Phil'ps end meetsiscase?'

'Because,' Whitehead tactfully removed the bottle of madeira from the outstretched hand of Mrs Phillips who having gone so far was emboldened by the luscious grape to go farther, 'your good husband would still be in the service of his Grace of Kingston had it not been for the mack – (no better not try that one again) the chick – (no, almost as bad) chick – ain'ry of the Duchess.'

'Her chick?' queried Mrs Phillips, not unnaturally befogged.

'Meaning – mischief-making shall we say as she has mish-mischief-made me and will mishchief-make you' (Whitehead had also gone about as far as he could go), 'and so we had best leave it at that, madam, an' don' say I haven't warned you.'

And we too had best leave it at that, Whitehead having done *his* best, or worst, to plant the seeds of misdoubt and mistrust in what remained of the fuddled mind of the poor little ex-parson's wife to reap a bitter harvest for Elizabeth, Duchess of Kingston.

*   *   *

Having sown the seeds of what he hopefully believed would result in disproving the Duke's marriage to the woman already the wife of another man, for Whitehead had convinced himself that a nullity of Hervey's marriage to Elizabeth Chudleigh would not hold closer investigation, he now awaited his dismissal. This, he was resigned to know, would be finally determined within the next few weeks.

It was.

The Kingstons were about to leave Thoresby for Bath. Elizabeth had word with Caesar Hawkins on her husband's health. He advised her that the waters of Bath would be beneficial. 'His weight,' Hawkins said, 'must be reduced and a stricter diet enforced with a minimum of spirituous liquors.'

Nothing to Kingston's approval was this, but as always Elizabeth had her way. 'And,' she told him, 'we can now dispose of Whitehead. I will not have him in charge of you or your diet nor your limited spirituous liquors. It is he who orders pipes of wine to be laid down, half of which none drinks except Whitehead. I am taking only a few of our servants, the first footman can valet you.'

Thus was all arranged if not to Kingston's satisfaction to hers in a letter from the Duke to Whitehead (dictated by Elizabeth) informing him that his services were no longer required. He was given a month's notice with a bonus of twenty pounds. 'Which,' Elizabeth told the reluctantly pliable Duke, 'is as much as he has had from you above his wages every few weeks in all these years laying down pipes of wine which you have been the last to drink.'

Then two days before their departure for Bath came a message from Leicester House that the Dowager Princess was at death's door.

Elizabeth arrived just in time to attend the Princess before she died. She was unconscious but rallied to recognize her favourite 'Elizabet', her pale lips framing the word before her eyelids sank.

She died on 8 February, 1772, and was carried to her grave amid the indecent rejoicing of the mob who some four years before had rioted in London's streets, the followers of Wilkes and the enemies of Bute. He, now retired to his island and his wife, did not return in time to witness the shocking scenes that attended the funeral of the King's mother. Huzzahing crowds surged forward to the entrance of the Abbey; they stripped the black cloths from the coffin and, defying the constables, attempted to force their way into the doors but were held back.

To what extent the King suffered these humiliating last rites of his mother who herself had suffered intolerable humiliation from her late husband, we cannot tell; but that he, this third George, owed much to his mother for his pietistic upbringing and careful supervision of his heritage advised by his 'dear friend Lord Bute' is certain. If he mourned his mother's death in private, which he did not in public other than to order Court mourning for a month, is not known. He had almost immediately another family misfortune to deal with that must have affected him even more than the loss of his mother who, as he knew, had been dying for the past year.

The latest calamity fallen on the King concerned Elizabeth far less than the loss of her friend and patroness, the Princess Augusta. This, the discovery by his horrified Majesty that his brother, William, Duke of Gloucester, had been secretly married. Six years. To another widow. Lady Waldegrave.

Appalling apocalypse!

It was known that her father-in-law, now deceased, had been one of the King's tutors in the days when Elizabeth had been the 'dear friend' and confidante of the then Prince of Wales, but what none other than Elizabeth knew was that William of Gloucester had been the King's favourite brother.

William was diametrically opposed to Henry of Cumberland, that rakish young devil who had got himself bedded and then wedded to Anne Horton, and banished from the King and his Court. Not that Henry cared a damn to have been banished from his brother's dreary Court and the perpetual hymn singing and Papendiek's everlasting flute, besides the perennial influx of nephews and nieces to the Royal nurseries. But William was a very different proposition from the disgraceful Henry.

The Duke of Gloucester was, as the King had always thought him to be, a serious, God-fearing young man, as high-principled as the King himself. And now. Married. These six years. To *another* widow. . . . The trick of repetition was never so apparent. Not, be it understood . . . *not* that, as in the case of the dastardly Henry, any imputation could be cast upon the virtue of Lady Waldegrave, but that she happened to have been born out of wedlock, the daughter of Horace Walpole's brother, Sir Edgar Walpole, and a little milliner . . . 'A nobod . . . A nobody. A com . . . a commoner. From nowhere. And she, William's wife, was now pregnant. Fourth. Fifth in – six – seventh in success – succession to . . . to the Throne!'

Thus we may suppose the King lamented to his equally horrified Charlotte, since we are told that 'he cried and lay awake all night'.

'There seems to be,' remarked Elizabeth, when she and the Duke were at Kingston House following the funeral of the Dowager Princess, 'a peculiar attraction for millinery among the *haut monde*.' An unkindly reminder of Kingston's interest in the young person of Cranbourne Alley. 'But Lady Waldegrave's mother,' Elizabeth dreamily resumed, 'could scarcely have been *your* little milliner unless, of course, she took off a good many years of her supposedly twenty odd?'

She had never quite forgotten nor did she intend to let him forget those visits to the little milliner who had engaged his imagination – shall we say? – for that one lapse of her devoted 'Evie's' attachment to herself.

But now that the apocalyptic delinquency of the King's

brother William ceased to be the subject of discussion in and out of Court, and the King, we presume, had wept himself dry, although he was noticeably more repetitive, more easily roused to a brainstorm, more pop-eyed and generally worried about this that or the other and all this trouble and growing unrest in his American colonies, and his good Lord North who *would* slobber when he spoke but was the best . . . quite the best. What? What? But quite, yes, quite the best Prime Minister, better than his good Lord Bute. What? . . . When the Kingstons, or rather Elizabeth, decided they had enough of the Court and the King, 'Who,' observed Kingston, 'if not yet entirely *non compos mentis* is well on the way to be', they made off for the journey to Bath.

Whitehead, who had taken his not unexpected dismissal with a martyred resignation that boded ill for 'that woman', was furthering his plans of action 'to be even with her when the time should be ripe to strike'. . . . According to Whitehead, who attended the Duke's departure with Elizabeth from Kingston House to Bath, 'she, her Disgrace', reported Whitehead to those of the reduced staff at Kingston House ('the clean sweep' had now begun), 'has bought a brace of pistols against highwaymen on the road to Bath, she *says*, but methinks the lady's precautions against any such attack are more likely to be directed at me!'

He did not elaborate on that assumption which went down well with those of the staff also under dismissal, since what he had in mind to avenge himself on 'that woman' for his severance from the Duke's service would be a far more serious indictment than her defence at pistol point against himself or any other, whether highwayman or not.

But the journey to Bath was unattended by any untoward interruption. They arrived at Abbey Bath House on the South Parade which Elizabeth had rented for this visit for the next three months.

They were received by the landlady, a Mrs Hodgkinson, with effusive welcome accompanied by the obsequious tributes due to persons of high rank. Although the Monarch of Bath, Beau Nash, had been dead these several years, the long Indian summer of Bath's heyday lingered nostalgically during this second half of the eighteenth century. Yet whereas before, when Nash reigned supreme, none but the *beau monde* flocked to the beautiful city poised above the Avon, now, however, if we may take Smollett's word for the decline of 'the Queen of the West': 'Every upstart of fortune, harnessed in the trappings of the mode, presents himself to Bath.'

Elizabeth noted with dismay that although the bells rang out to announce their arrival, following the custom inaugurated by the Beau to proclaim the visit of august personages, those same bells now rang for all sorts, providing they were known to be sufficiently affluent. Planters from American cotton fields, wives and daughters of wealthy tradesmen, a busy jostling crowd of *nouveaux riches*, superimposed upon the exclusive province of the high-born. This was the Bath of Sheridan and Smollett, but still the golden age of the Beau's influence on architecture persisted, with the building of Royal Crescent yet to be completed when the Kingstons came to Bath. Although the Duke had often been there in the days of Nash, Elizabeth had never made more than the briefest of visits when Prince Frederick of Wales and the Princess had come with Elizabeth in attendance as recently appointed Maid of Honour before her marriage to Hervey.

Caesar Hawkins had advised Elizabeth to induce the Duke to take the waters, which he was loth to do but, as ever guided by her, he agreed, and they were to be seen in the Pump Room every morning. It cannot be said that Elizabeth enjoyed rubbing shoulders with those who were hail-fellow-well-met among the latest visitors to be rung in. 'Charlatans and mountebanks,' she complained to

Kingston, 'a lot of shovel-nosed sharks attempting to emulate US . . .'

She had never outgrown her gratification at being addressed as 'Your Grace', although custom had staled the novelty.

Kingston, as he sat in his corner tumbler in hand, mildly suggested: 'I can't see why, just because they've made a fortune from tea, cotton, sugar or whatever else in the American colonies or in the Indies, you should liken them to double-nosed sharks.'

She did not pursue that subject further; she had in fact hardly heard him for her attention was diverted by the entrance of an exceedingly lovely young girl accompanied by an equally attractive young gentleman.

'Is not that young lady –' Elizabeth had of late acquired a quizzing glass adopted by women of fashion emulating their menfolk – 'do you see her?' she spoke to Kingston without turning her head, the glass on its tortoiseshell handle to her eye, 'I am sure she is the Linley girl, and that young man with her – he must be Sheridan's son.'

'Sheridan?' Kingston gulped the last of the atrocious water, retched, hiccupped, kept it down and said: 'Who's Sheridan?'

'Nobody in particular. A play-actor fellow who teaches elocution here. And that son of his whom you see with the Linley girl has written or is writing a play that may be seen on the London stage. Quite a talented young man, they say.'

Elizabeth made it her business to know everyone's business as well as her own. And to while away the somewhat tedious days at the Bath, where few of her Court circle were much in evidence at this time, she had met and chose to renew her acquaintance with one of her quondam friends and Maids of Honour, Mistress Ashe who had married disastrously Lady Mary Wortley Montagu's son and a cousin of Kingston's. That marriage, another hasty elopement, ended with Wortley Montagu's arrest for

175

having won five hundred Louis d'or off a rich Jew in Paris. Plied with drink until he was incapable of knowing one card from another, and, after finding he had been cheated, the Jew refused to pay the winnings of Wortley Montagu and his associates. They then threatened him with their swords, whereupon the Jew made out a draft on a Paris banker with whom he had no dealings, aware that the bill would be dishonoured. Discovering they had been duped, Wortley Montagu and his equally disreputable friends broke into the Jew's house, rifled his safe and strong boxes, robbed him of money and valuable jewellery and were arrested. Imprisoned in the Grand Châtelet for three or four months they were finally acquitted, sentence being passed upon the victimized Jewish gentleman to make reparation and repay all costs.

Elizabeth, who left her husband to imbibe the waters, had gone shopping in Milsom Street to buy a hat for herself and a snuff box for Kingston. Emerging from the silversmith's with the snuff box – 'to be paid for' (by Evie, of course) 'if you will call at the Abbey Bath House,' she told the bowing silversmith, 'when I, the Duchess of Kingston, will give you the money for it which I have not about me now.' More bowings and hand-washings from the silversmith who had heard the bells rung in for the arrival of their Graces of Kingston the week before; not so often these days were the shopkeepers of Bath patronized by Duchesses. And as Elizabeth turned toward the Pump Room she heard in a shrill, slightly cracked treble:

'Gracious goodness! If it isn't the Chudleigh!'

It was Elizabeth Ashe, Mrs Wortley Montagu, instantly recognized; and although she had lost her youthful sprightliness she still retained the charmful fascination that had enslaved so many of the gilded youth in the days of Frederick of Wales. But the passing of years that had left scarcely a trace on the flawless skin and brilliant blue of the Chudleigh's eyes had been less kindly to this other and equally notorious Elizabeth.

'Let us,' she chirped, 'go into Gill's for a taste of his Bath buns.'

The shop of Mr Gill, the pastry-cook, most favoured by the ladies, was hard by the Pump Room; and there the feminine habituées of Gill's would meet to chat, exchange gossip and the talk of the town while partaking of a jelly, or one of the Bath buns that have lived through the centuries, or a dish of Gill's delicious vermicelli. He greeted these two Elizabeths with the fawning affability he bestowed upon all of the higher rank to distinguish those of the 'plebs', as Mr Gill disdainfully would allude to the ostentatious newcomers whom Smollett had described as 'Whales of Fortune'. And while he called an underling to take the ladies' order, he allowed those lesser beings who were staring agape at the two newcomers, so obviously of the high world, to learn that one of these fashionable ladies was addressed by Gill with much display of palpably false teeth, as 'Your Grace'.

'So you've got there at last,' remarked the former Mistress Ashe, spooning a mouthful of pink jelly, accompaniment of a Bath bun.

'Where you,' returned the former Mistress Chudleigh, all smiles, 'and never for the want of trying, did approach more than an arm's or should one say bed's length?'

'You were always so sharp, my dear Chudleigh.' The good-humoured Ashe was never one to take offence however much she could and did offend. 'But you stayed well placed in *your* bed's length. How is he, may one ask? I've heard he is ordered here for the waters. Gout or too much wedlocked pleasuring?'

'Neither.' Elizabeth's smile stayed a trifle too widely stretched but her teeth were all her own, unlike Mr Gill's or indeed those of the fair Mistress Ashe who chose to revert to her unmaidenly maiden name, since that of her husband had reeked through Paris to turn the stomachs of London's Courts. 'Kingston has always been moderate in both wine and women.'

'One heard differently when I was a girl and he forty years younger. Another bun,' she beckoned the hovering Gill.

'But certainly, your ladyship.'

'Not I "your ladyship" yet,' she treated him to her still youthful and mischievous grin, 'but as the Duchess has so rightly observed, not for the want of trying. There is still hope if my husband should land himself in any more trouble in Paris.'

'I wonder,' reproved Elizabeth, 'that you can mention your husband's disgrace to Gill to have it blown all over the town. Don't forget that Wortley Montagu is Kingston's cousin. He took it hardly that one of his kin should have brought shame upon his name.'

'Not Kingston's name,' said Mrs Wortley Montagu, 'his mother's name, or rather his father's name since his mother was a Pierrepoint. And why in the devil – and the devil was in it, believe me – when having been diddled by that Jew he had the tables turned on him and those other two who robbed Ikey Mo. Not so much of an Ikey Mo either, he is of a good old banking family I hear, and could well afford to lose a few hundred Louis d'or and some of his hoarded jewels. I see you are not taking a bun. I can eat as many as I want for I have the sweetest tooth.'

Elizabeth reddened beneath her rouge. She had been quick to note that the passage of time had not added with its years any superabundance of flesh to the sylphlike, if slightly too angular a figure of her erstwhile friend. The same, regretfully, could not be said of Elizabeth, Duchess of Kingston, who showed little of Pulteney's 'divinity' and Walpole's 'nymph' in her ever so slight but carefully disguised embonpoint.

'Well, I hope we shall see much of each other,' said Mrs Ashe-Wortley Montagu, 'now we are met together again. I am here, not for the waters but,' she coyly giggled, 'at urgent desire of Lord Granby. You know him,

178

I believe, since he lives almost next door to you in Knightsbridge. Must you go?'

Elizabeth must go; she had more than her fill of the Ashe and could not but be satisfied to see that the once glowing cheeks of girlhood had fallen in 'as her teeth', remarked the Duchess to her inner Grace, 'have fallen out'.

So with mutual expressions of delight at this 'so unexpected and longed for – yes, I've longed to be re-united to my dear Mrs Chudleigh whom I have not seen these many years', twittered the other Elizabeth as they parted to go their separate ways.

When she returned to the Pump Room where she had left Kingston taking his daily dose of the waters, she saw that the seat in his customary corner was vacant. On inquiring of an attendant he told her that his Grace had sent for his servant to bring a chair as he was not feeling well and wished to go back to his lodgings.

In great alarm Elizabeth ordered a chair and was conveyed to the house on the South Parade. There her maid, Elizabeth, one of the three she had brought with her, said:

'His Grace – we – his man got him to bed and sent for the doctor. He was taken poorly just after you left his Grace at the Pump Room.'

Elizabeth ran upstairs to the bedroom. The doctor was with him. He turned as she entered and immediately set her mind at rest.

'I have advised his Grace to suspend taking the waters which it would seem do nauseate him to that extent that they defeat their ends.'

'What', she asked, her stiffened lips relaxed, 'caused him to send for a chair to bring him back without waiting for me?'

'A palpitation of the heart accompanied by vomiting. It is not unusual,' he assured her, 'when the patient takes an aversion to the waters. I prescribe complete rest for the next few days.'

She was enormously relieved for she had reproached herself having left him to take the waters, which she knew he abhorred, without her at his side.

He did not seem to be any the worse for his slight indisposition although Doctor Rains, whom Kingston insisted should accompany them from Thoresby, having a great opinion of and confidence in him as his medical adviser, had told her that the symptoms which had attacked him, although slight, might recur with more serious effect.

For the next week she watched over him and would allow none, not even his valet Williams who had replaced Whitehead, to attend his smallest needs and none but she must supervise his meals. Only the lightest of dishes, custards, fish, no red meat had been ordered by Dr Rains. Then on the fourth day of his illness he surprised her by asking that Whitehead should be sent for.

Whitehead, having been informed by one of the servants who accompanied the Kingstons from Thoresby and had been well supplied with remuneration for any news concerning their Graces and in particular *her* Grace, was already in Bath and lodged at the house where, on their arrival, rooms had been engaged. But finding them unsatisfactory Elizabeth had removed her husband, herself and such of her staff as she deemed necessary, to the Abbey Bath House. Both these lodgings were owned by the same landlady, Mrs Hodgkinson, although a subordinate had been in charge of the Orange Grove apartments.

Whitehead had made good use of his time by enlivening the notes for his subsequent damnifying letters accusing the Duchess of having aggravated his Grace's condition by 'continuous vexation to his nerves that suffered from matrimonial discontent'. He enlarges upon these suppositions by affirming that he heard the Duke from the top of the stairs demanding: 'Where is Whitehead?' This is obviously impossible since Kingston was confined to his bed nowhere near the stairs and had scarcely the voice to speak, being now in a state of semi-coma due to what Dr Rains diagnosed as an apoplexy, a recurrence with more serious effect than that which had at first attacked him, attended by a palsy on the whole of the right side with a distortion of the mouth and the right eye.

'Hearing the Duke ask for me,' continues the imaginative Whitehead, 'I instantly rushed past the Duchess who would have stopped me on the staircase, and I met the good Duke with tears in his eyes. I never saw a man so altered in so short a time. The Duchess hurried him into his chair (Kingston already bedridden and dying), 'obliging me to go away; and I never spoke to him afterwards'.... All this was sheer fabrication on the part of Whitehead but he made good use of it when a few days later Kingston died.

Elizabeth had never left him day or night, until at the last his closed eyes opened; his lips moved to a whisper ... 'My love ... my wife ...' And she on her knees beside him: 'Your wife and my love, now and for ever. Together always ...'

EIGHT

No sympathy was offered to the grief-stricken widow. 'The Duchess is a miracle of moderation,' records Walpole, bound to be in at the death. 'She has only taken the whole of the Duke's real and his personal estate for her life. Evelyn Medows is totally disinherited.'

This was the first allusion to Evelyn Medows, of whom we shall hear more, to Elizabeth's final subversion.

Friendless now that the Dowager Princess could no longer support her, even the customary mourning with all its exaggerated ceremonies due to persons of rank in this eighteenth century were scoffed at by her censorious enemies. Because the Duke had died at Bath instead of in his home he could not lie in state at Holme Pierrepoint, where he was taken to be laid in the vault of his forefathers, but with the due respect for his rank she ordered that the house at Bath should be hung with black, that all the servants should wear mourning, even the kitchenmaids had to rub their pots and pans with black cloths to cause great amusement when circulated by Whitehead on his return to London. He had further grievance to hoard against Elizabeth . . . 'Being desired by the Duchess to attend the funeral' (a kindly concession on her part for which Whitehead did not thank her), 'I made no doubt of her Grace's reimbursement for putting myself in mourning but I never got a sixpence for my trouble. . . . I wrote several times to the Duchess and never could obtain an answer.'

If she did not provide him with a sixpence for his mourning she rightly assumed he had accumulated sufficient 'sixpences' during his service with her late husband to pay for it, or that he probably had a wardrobe of black purloined from his master who had a supply of all necessary funeral trappings. But Whitehead was not content to be deprived of his many sixpences (or guineas) out of respect to his late master's remains. He added another mark against her to revenge himself on 'the wicked designing woman' who he was pursuaded had lost him his 'long devoted service to his Grace'.

Thanks to his untiring efforts, Whitehead managed to render Elizabeth's position in Court circles a perpetual embarrassment after the death of her husband.

Much of this related to Kingston's Will of which Whitehead, who we know had made himself acquainted with the Duke's private papers, had discovered:

'The last Will and testament of Me, Evelyn Pierrepoint, Duke of Kingston' [read and well digested word for word by Whitehead] 'do by this Will ratify and confirm which I made of the annual sum of Four thousand Pounds on my wife Elizabeth, Duchess of Kingston. ... And my said Wife shall be permitted during her widowhood to receive and take the yearly rents and profits of all the manors and lands as shall grow due during her widowhood but in case my said wife shall determine her widowhood during her life then I shall give and devise the same to Charles Medows second son of William Medows.

Also I bequeath to my said wife Elizabeth Duchess of Kingston all my furniture, pictures, plate, jewels and all other of my effects and personal estate for her own proper use absolutely for evermore. . . .'

This is the Will, of which Whitehead declares that: 'Forseeing what might be the consequent of the Duke's death should she survive him, the wary Duchess caused him to write every word of the Will in his own hand. . . .'

The result of which, with his whole estate hers absolutely and the enjoyment of Kingston's landed property for life, plus her four thousand annuity, would assure her an income of almost twenty thousand a year.

No mention in the Will had been made of Evelyn Medows, the Duke's direct heir in all but his title which died with him. That Kingston had made his Will in favour of his wife, which surely any husband would rightly execute for the woman he loved and who had devoted herself to him both as mistress and his lawful Duchess, sent Whitehead at once to acquaint Evelyn Medows with the contents of the Will.

This Evelyn Medows, Kingston's nephew, was the eldest son of Philip Medows who had married Lady Frances Pierrepoint, sister of the Duke of Kingston; but they had not been on the best of terms together and had not seen each other for years.

Elizabeth was fully aware of the discussions concerning her husband's Will and the inferences that she had induced him to disinherit his nephew and next of kin in her favour. It was also buzzed about that Kingston had not been responsible when signing the Will as he was dying and barely conscious at the time. All of these spiteful slings at her, activated by Whitehead, were entirely false as the Will had been made immediately after Kingston's marriage and Elizabeth knew nothing of it until he divulged to her its contents.

So soon as she could leave Kingston House when all to do with the probate and various other matters had been settled between herself and her attorney, Mr Field, she went back to Thoresby.

And in the aching loneliness of her loss she realized, and how regretfully, that she had never loved him so much as now that he was gone from her. If only, she cried in her heart, I had let him see how much he meant to me! She feared he believed his title had been his chief attraction. No denying that might have been so during the first years of their association, but as time went on and long before their marriage his dukedom had lost its glamour for her. It was the man she loved – if only she could have shown him how this gentle gentleman so strangely unsophisticated had won her warm and devoted regard. He needed her, and she, as with her Princess who also needed her affection and loyalty, had never failed him.

Memories came about her in clouds of remorse as she wandered in her loneliness beside the lake where they had so often walked together hand in hand.

But although Thoresby held for her all she had cherished in these few years of her marriage, because only since she had become his wife in name did she feel herself to belong to Thoresby, she felt she must break away for at least a year or two and try to readjust her life and find some distraction from perpetual emptiness and lack of love and kindly comradeship. . . . Why, she wondered, had she, who had always been receptive to the proffered hand of friendship from women – not men who asked of her anything but friendship – only succeeded in making enemies? Jealousy? Why should she be the victim of jealousy who had never wished ill of anyone? Is it my fault, she asked herself, that men have sought me? Why? I gave them nothing, not as my associates at Court did give and offered more than was desired. She knew she was less beautiful than many others who had not achieved the material success that she had won. Not given to self-analysis, she could not know that what Pulteney had found in her which overcame her trivial superficialities, her childish greed for life's luxuries that went with wealth and rank, was her indomitable courage and eager receptivity, even though she had made no effort to disguise how Pulteney's attempt to inculcate the rudiments of scholarship into the simple country girl whom he discovered in a Devonshire lane had bored her.

She had admitted with laughter, and she could laugh at herself which was one of her endearing qualities that:

'I should hate myself if I were in the same mood for two hours together. . . .'

It was on a wintry frost-rimed day with a dim sun stealing through the barren trees of the encircling Sherwood forest. The pallid light of that sun-lost morning lay reflected on the ice-fringed lake when an encounter, as if sprung from a long forgotten past, crossed her way as she wandered there in solitude.

She heard her name called, 'Your Grace', and swung round to see standing in the path behind her a woman whom at first she did not recognize until, 'Madam, your Grace', was repeated, and then:

'Why – is it? It *is* Anne Craddock!'

Anne Craddock it was, grown stouter, older, greyer, but the same Anne Craddock who had come to her at Chelsea before she had her baby. 'How did you manage to find me here after all these years?' She could not but feel some doubt at this unbidden reappearance of the one woman other than Mrs Amis who had known of her hasty marriage to Hervey in that little chapel at Lainston and which had been proven null and void. Did Anne know that? she wondered.

'I have taken the liberty, madam – Your Grace,' said Anne folding her arms across her chest and with a look that held in it something of challenge accompanied by the tone of her voice which was a bare stave or two from a menace – 'if your Grace will excuse me, of comin' all this way by the coach me 'avin' been told at Kingston House as you was 'ere at Thoresby, to offer you my condolence on your sad b'reavement.'

Elizabeth, at once beguiled, as always when any indication of sympathy was offered, readily replied:

'That is very kind of you. But how did you know to find me here?'

'I was told by the footman up at the 'ouse that you walk by the lake so I came along to see.'

'Come back to the house,' Elizabeth's first impulse of

doubt discarded in the warmth of her greeting to the woman who had known and had apparently shared in her grief at the loss of her son. Yes, and she had taken her to see that small, so small a grave where he lay in the church-yard at Chelsea and had comforted her tears as they fell on the flowers she had brought to plant there. 'I am so glad you have come to me. You must stay awhile here at Thoresby. I leave soon for Italy – Rome. I find the lone-liness here unbearable but I would be thankful to have you here with me until I leave – that is if you can spare the time? I heard you had married.'

'Yes, I was married but my husband died. He was in the service of your hus – of Mr Hervey. But I still call myself by my maiden name. He – we – it was not you might say a happy or real marriage as,' again that slight challenge, 'your Grace will understand.'

'Mine was no marriage,' Elizabeth did not enlarge on that. She had no wish to open old sores of which Anne, she believed, could know nothing. 'It is so good of you,' she said gratefully, 'to have sought me out.'

Too trusting, too innocently unsuspicious, despite her worldly-wise experience, Elizabeth brought into her house and into her generous heart the woman whom she could not possibly have known was a pawn in the hands of those who were bent on her betrayal.

So into the servants' hall was Anne conducted and regaled with the best the board could offer her. Another false attribute circulated by Whitehead had been that, 'the woman who *claimed* to be the Duchess of Kingston, was niggardly and ill-treated her servants, abused them in shocking language and kept them short of victuals'.

If Anne had been primed, as she certainly must have been, by Whitehead's reports of the households in the Duke's domains and the alleged parsimony practised by the Duchess, she may have been surprised to find her-self served with a liberality unusual either in the household of Mr Hervey or, in years past, when in service with the late Mrs Hanmer.

The steward who had replaced the late Duke's butler saw to it that neither he nor his understaff should want – and this at her Grace's request – in any sufficiency of food or drink, for although she had restrained Whitehead's unlimited perquisites, she ordered the requirements of her servants in accordance with the salaries she paid for good service. The 'clean sweep', on which she had insisted when she married Kingston, had brought her an army of well-trained and well-paid domestics who performed their duties to her Grace's satisfaction and with due reward.

When Anne Craddock had been well dined and supplied with a bumper of ale, Elizabeth sent for her. She came with curtsies, 'Your Grace bids me –?'

'That, as I have offered, you must stay here until I leave for Rome. After all, you are the only soul alive who knew of my son before –' her voice faltered – 'before I lost him.'

'All except Mrs Amis,' was said in that same half-menacing tone.

'You have seen Mrs Amis – Mrs Phillips as she is now?'

'Once or twice, madam, when I am in London.'

'Do you live in London?'

'I wish to live there rather than be buried in the country.'

'I was about to suggest that you return to your native village which, if I remember rightly, was in – was it Derbyshire?'

'No, madam, I was born in Derbyshire but have no liking to live buried in the country. I have little enough to live on, but in London I can obtain work as housekeeper to a single gentleman or to Captain Medows who has expressed the wish to have me serve him.'

'Captain Medows?'

'It was Mr Whitehead who recommended me to Captain Medows as is in need of a housekeeper, and it is also through Mr Whitehead that I heard of your Grace's loss.'

'If you were in London I should have thought you would have heard of my loss long before this. It is now five months since his Grace died at Bath.' Elizabeth was beginning to have her doubts as to the sincerity of Anne Craddock's visit of condolence since the mention of Medows, the Duke's nephew who she knew had been cut out of her husband's Will, started an alarm bell in the corridors of suspicion.... Whitehead and Medows. The two names spelt danger. She mustered a premonitory ambuscade against what she sensed to be a conspiratorial attack from Medows engineered by Whitehead using Anne as their tool.

The antennae of suspicion, now aroused, pointed the gently lubricated query:

'Does Captain Medows offer you a handsome salary for your service as his housekeeper?'

'A mere stipend, madam, of thirty pounds a year. But,' Anne lowered her eyes and added with a snuffle, 'if your Grace would take me into your service that I could attend on you in London or here at Thoresby, I would gladly accept twenty pounds a year for the honour of serving your Grace.'

'And at the same time to have the honour of serving Captain Medows with whatever information you can gather from my personal affairs and correspondence, so that you can return to him who sends you to me with more than your coach fare, I presume?'

'No, your Grace! No!' Anne, seeing herself cornered, produced not very well simulated tears. 'I have received not one penny from Captain Medows – not until I enter his service.'

'Are you not now in his service? Or,' Elizabeth moved towards the bell-rope on the wall, 'does he wait to learn the result of your visit to me?'

'How – oh – how your Grace', Anne manufactured

sobs, 'does misunderstand me. I came here of my own good will to offer my condolence and to serve your Grace with all my heart if you would take me for old times' sake and to aid my poor means which I can swear do give me barely enough to live on. But I would gladly accept twenty pounds a year from your Grace whom I know or used to know so well – just for old times' sake.'

'Old times,' Elizabeth pulled the bell-rope, 'have a trick of recurring as you have made clear and, as has been said, the whirligig of time brings in its revenges. As for the penny Captain Medows denies you until you enter his service in which I gather you already are employed by him who sends you here, you will not get a penny from me more than your coach fare to London or from whatever devil's inferno you have come.'

It was rash of her to show her hand but as always reckless and, as she often declared, 'What's on my lung must come out on my tongue,' she did not think before she spoke. And to the footman who answered her summons:

'Order the gig to take Craddock to the inn where the stage coach stops – when?'

'Within the hour, your Grace.'

'Very well. Tell the steward to give you the coach fare to be paid to the woman Craddock for her return journey to London. You will go with her to the coach and see that she secures a seat on it.'

Her maid Elizabeth came to her when Anne Craddock had been disposed of, saying:

'Your Grace, pray forgive this intrusion but I feel I must warn you that the woman Craddock means you mischief. She was telling us at table certain talk that I – and most of us – resented. To do with what Whitehead had let fall of your Grace's interference with his Grace's Will.'

'This is no surprise to me, my dear.' Elizabeth took the girl's hand in hers. 'I admit that at first when she accosted me by the lake I was ready to believe her good intent, but

I have learned to trust none who comes to me with fair words and fulsome offers of goodwill. None save yourself, and perhaps some of the staff whom I have reason to hope are loyal.'

'You have good reason, your Grace, to be cautious I –'

A fit of coughing stayed her words. Elizabeth looked at her anxiously.

'This cough – it has been with you all the winter since you went down sick of that tertian fever. Dr Rains said it had left you with a slight chest congestion and he prescribed you plentiful milk and a tincture to take at night. I hope you follow his advice?'

'Yes, your Grace. This cough is nothing. I have had a rheum in the head, but I am quite myself again.'

'You must be careful in this cold weather to wrap up well when you go out. But as for Anne Craddock and the mischief she would have made in the short while she sat at table with the staff, I did intend to take you with me to Rome, but, my love, as you are the only one of my servants whom I know to be the most loyal –'

'As I am, your Grace,' the girl, a frail young thing with a skin so transparent the delicate blue veins showed through on her temples like the markings of skeleton leaves, and on her cheeks a glow of eggshell pink – 'I am indeed. Do I not owe my very existence to your dear mother who took me and brought me up as her own when I was left abandoned at her door in Windsor Castle? And has not your Grace been to me also as a mother – having never known any more than your and Mrs Chudleigh's protection?'

The girl's eyes were bright with tears.

'Because I regard you as did my mother as if you were my own I cannot – this will hurt you, my dear – but I have to say it, I cannot take you with me abroad next week. I leave you here in charge so you may report to me anything or anybody that may strike you as with ill intent, or any visitors unknown to you from hereabouts that may inquire of my address abroad. You can write to Mr Fielding who will be in charge of the staff at Kingston House, and the steward at Holme Pierrepoint will be informed how to deal with strangers. . . . My dear child,' she had seen a suppressed tear falling. 'I realize what a disappointment this must be to you that I cannot have you with me on my travels, but it will not be for long and I am sure you would sooner safeguard me here than leave Thoresby to the careless charge of any other than yourself.'

The girl was on her knees to her.

'Your Grace,' she buried her head in Elizabeth's gown, 'you may be sure of that. I would have no moment's peace if I thought I had failed you in my duty to guard your Grace from all ill-wishers.'

'Of whom,' she raised her up, 'there are too many. God bless you, my child,' she kissed the girl's cheek where a tear had fallen. 'I would so much rather have had you with me than any of the other maids, for in truth,' she slid an arm round the thin – too thin? – shoulders, 'you are *my* Maid of Honour.'

'I thank your Grace, and that too,' the girl achieved a watery smile, 'Anne Craddock told us in the servants' hall, jesting of it as she made out, that your Grace which Whitehead – that snake –' The girl spat out the word with a clenching of her small front teeth – 'he had told her that your Grace thinks of yourself as a queen whose name should be – No!' she covered her mouth, 'I cannot say it.'

'I think I can guess the name that Whitehead – a boa-constrictor rather than an ordinary harmless snake-in-the-grass – commissioned Anne Craddock to name me. Jezebel was it? But Whitehead professes to have some acquired learning of the classics and knows less than nothing of the Bible, for Jezebel was no queen unless queen of the whores! My dear, do not allow yourself one moment's anxiety on the serpentine Whitehead's venom

192

directed at me. I have him well marked and am provided with ample antidote against his poison.'

Elizabeth was sad to part from this one of all her servants upon whom she knew she could rely for her fidelity and love; she who, until her life with Kingston, had never known love and loyalty, not even though Hamilton had youthfully sworn to her his adoration and betrothal. She had often thought had they been man and wife he might have tired and turned from her. That he had been so easily consoled in marrying the Gunning girl was proof enough. Nor did that marriage fulfil the bridegroom's expectations, as Elizabeth was not disappointed to hear.

At the time of Elizabeth's visit to Rome, Clement XIV, recently elected Pope, was at the height of his pontifical power and respected throughout Europe. While preserving the pomp and ceremony due to his papal authority he combined the simplicity of character and the broad-minded approach to his subjects that had gained him the affection of all who knew him when he was Father Ganganelli, and with that twist of humour which made him so beloved he would say: 'I have been a prince and a pope all day and so that I may not be quite suffocated, let me now be Father Ganganelli again.'

Elizabeth had managed to win the regard of Frederick the Great, and later, when on her travels, of Catherine II of Russia, therefore it is not surprising that almost immediately she arrived in Rome she was received by Pope Clement. At once perceiving an original after his own heart, he welcomed her with the utmost cordiality. She had come prepared to be seen and to conquer, having built for herself a splendid pleasure yacht captained by an ex-naval officer. With twenty thousand a year she could afford to gratify her every extravagant whim. She came with a retinue of attendants and various objets d'art from Kingston's collection – hers now – pictures, jewels, and a wardrobe of gowns that would have bitterly excited the envy of ladies in the London Courts.

Ganganelli, as so many other men before him, was charmed by her ready wit, her vivacity and her unconventionality that appealed to one who confessed himself 'suffocated' by the ceremonious splendour of his pontifical rank.

He endowed her with privileges accorded only to princes, and placed at her disposal one of the cardinals' palaces during her visit to Rome. She was in her element; her sorrow at the loss of her Duke soothed, if not healed, by the reception offered her by the highest in Roman society from Pope Clement downward. If, as those who have decried her as a scheming adventuress, she were tolerated solely because of her wealth she would certainly not have been so lavishly entertained, if entertained at all. She returned fourfold the hospitality she received, spending money right and left for the benefit of the city's tradespeople, who drew enormous profits from her purchases that year. There was no limit to her reciprocal gestures of courtesy. She ordered the captain of her yacht to sail up the Tiber to the delight of the vast cheering crowd who had never seen anything to equal the magnificence of this great English Duchess's entourage. She gave a succession of balls and fêtes and it would seem, were she to continue at this rate, she would lose more than half of her inherited wealth. Much she cared if she were lost of some several thousands! She had achieved the pinnacle of her ambition. Not only was she accepted in accordance with her rank as an English peeress, second only to royalty in her native land, but when she visited Florence she met with the same pomp and circumstance as in Rome. Reports came of her wonderful pageantry and astonishing expenditure, such as having bought a theatre in Rome for which she admitted that the salaries of the actors, singers, and dancers cost her 'as much or more than the revenue of some Italian states'! One night she had the entire Colosseum illuminated for the populace.

Small wonder she went accompanied by cheers and salutes as if she were in truth a queen.

Among those of her admirers who remained her staunch friend through all her trials was no man, but a woman; none other than the Electress Dowager of Saxony to whom she was presented in Florence. And then, while in Florence, rumours reached her that sent her back to Rome to assemble some of her attendants she had left in the cardinal's palace, to accompany her to London on a hurried visit to consult with her attorney, Mr Field.

Evelyn Medows, having heard how his uncle's 'woman' (never his wife, according to Medows) was flinging away his, Medows', rightful inheritance determined to dispute the Duke of Kingston's Will.

The fat was in the fire, but the fire was slow to burn, and when it did it roared in a blaze throughout the country.

*   *   *

In London her lawyer told her that Medows was threatening not only to dispute the Will but to challenge the validity of her marriage to his uncle.

'But he can't!' she declared. 'How can he challenge the decision of the Ecclesiastical Court that proved my marriage to Hervey null and void?'

The lawyer, a thin pawky-faced fellow with shrewd, intelligent eyes and bushy brows under a high dome-shaped forehead crowned by a powdered tie-wig, thumbed his chin.

'That remains to be seen. He will have to try for it and I have reason to believe he has already laid a case before Counsel who advises a charge of bigamy to be brought against your Grace.'

'Bigamy!' The colour fled from her cheeks under the light application of rouge. 'That is impossible. I am – I was the Duke's lawful wife!'

'Ex-actly.' The judicious voice of the attorney weighed

the word as if in two syllables while fixing an eye on a corner of the ceiling, ornamented with a moulding of fruit and some unspecified species of foliage. 'If that event should arise, we will counteract any such charge since we can produce the indubitable judgement of the Ecclesiastical Court.'

'I hope,' she fervently twisted her hands together, 'you are not too optimistic. I have to tell you I had a visit from Anne Craddock at Thoresby. She said –'

Elizabeth unfolded in brief what Anne had said.

Field shook his head.

'That savours of blackmail which is all in your favour. If this woman Craddock is prepared to receive from you a yearly sum of twenty pounds per annum in preference to the thirty she is offered by Medows, it points to the fact that she came to you for the purpose of running with the hare – shall we say? – and hunting with the hounds. It is evident she has in mind to disclose to Medows all she knows regarding your marriage to Hervey proven as no marriage for – a consideration. You did not, I trust, offer her any money to hold her tongue?'

'Good heavens, no! I sent her out of the house and all she had from me was her fare back to London by stage coach.'

'Then you may be sure she will go straight to Medows.'

'And then what?' Again the pink that had returned to her pallor receded. 'Would not her evidence that she saw me married to Hervey support his charge?'

'She did not see you married to Hervey. She was not in the church and there is none alive to bear witness to the ceremony.' (And she thought, I burnt whatever evidence there might have been. But she did not tell him this.)

'So, leave all to me, your Grace. Medows can do his worst and so I promise you can we, to set at defiance his attempt to bring a bill of indictment against you. Go back to Rome. You are in need of relaxation from your trials and sad bereavement.'

If Field's advice she should leave all to him was less to her advantage than he promised, she could not have foreseen that he unfortunately mismanaged and ill-advised the case. It might have served Elizabeth better had she silenced Anne Craddock with the sum or double that demanded to hold her tongue and range herself on the side of the Duchess. Instead Anne went, as Field surmised, straight back to Medows with the evidence of Elizabeth's marriage in writing.

That Field had banked on the decision of the Ecclesiastical Court was not proof enough to vindicate a charge of felony against Elizabeth for having bigamously married the Duke of Kingston. But this she could not know nor, when back in Rome believing all had been settled in her favour to deprive Medows of his attempted suit, did she give another thought to the cumbrous machinery of law set in action against her.

Walpole who, of course, had learned of her hurried visit to London and the charge Medows intended to bring disproving her marriage to Kingston, was at it again, writing to his friend Horace Mann : 'The bigamist Duchess is likely to become a real peeress at last. Lord Bristol has been struck with a palsy. . . . If he dies and Hervey should take a fancy to marry again as he did two or three years ago, his next brother [Bristol's immediate heir] may happen to assist the Duke of Kingston's relatives with proofs of Hervey's first marriage. But law is a horrid liar. . . .'

When a few months later the Earl of Bristol who had been so long dying did at last die and his brother Augustus succeeded him, Elizabeth, secure in her peerage as Duchess, stayed in Rome feeling perfectly safe from the 'horrid liar' the law, and with no wish to be deprived of her right as the Duchess of Kingston in preference to the lower rank of Countess of Bristol.

Walpole was again to the fore with his usual cynical comments : 'Will her Grace of Kingston condescend to be as she really is Countess of Bristol *alias* Duchess of Kingston to come into court?'

It was on everybody's tongue, all except Elizabeth's, that a bill of indictment for bigamy had been instituted against the Duchess, and a grand jury gave notice that unless the Duchess of Kingston appeared in time to plead her case, she would be subjected to a process of outlawry.

The first intimation of this thunderbolt fallen upon her out of an Italian summer's sky came by special messenger to Elizabeth in the cardinal's palace at Rome.

Field, her attorney, who had consulted Counsel, took his advice urging the Duchess's immediate return to England.

After the initial shock of this message, delivered by a dusty hard-riding emissary of the law who had travelled part of the way by diligence, Elizabeth, thrusting aside the dire possibilities suggested by Field's messenger, rose with that same intrepidity which had served her to confront worse and more factual danger as on her never-to-be-forgotten wedding night. It would need all her courage to face what lay before her. It is evident that Medows meant to bring about her downfall by claiming what he thought and may have rightly believed to be his and not her inheritance. It must rest upon her alone, her determination and true belief that she could prove to be Kingston's lawful wife.

She had lodged the bulk of her securities with her English banker, Jenkins, in Rome. Although she had been frittering away money to indulge her many extravagances she was inherently generous, notwithstanding the accusations of Whitehead and others who decried her as 'mean'. She had always been ready to give and would spend as much on gifts to those whom she thought were her friends as she ever had spent on herself.

So, realizing that her journey with sufficient attendants would cost more ready money than she had at hand, for she intended to leave her yacht on the Tiber, she called on Jenkins at his house, to be told he was not at home.

Now this Jenkins who started as a dealer of antiques in Rome, selling both the real and fakes to tourists, had established himself as banker for English visitors.

With him Elizabeth had placed some of her most valuable jewels as well as vast sums of money for fear she might be robbed, as all Rome knew of her wealth and her magnificent jewels. To this same end for the protection of her property and person, she had by her always the brace of pistols with which Whitehead reported she slept under her pillow at Thoresby.

When an hour or so later she again called on Jenkins and was again told by his servant that Mr Jenkins could not (or would not, she thought) see her, she became suspicious. It struck her that this Jenkins, whose reputation as she learned too late was not of the most reliable had, in all probability, been bribed by Medows to delay her return to England thereby rendering her subject to outlawry which, should judgement be obtained, would entail the confiscation of her property. This, although it would not have advantaged the Duke of Kingston's next of kin, would have been paid into His Majesty's Exchequer.

She went back to her palace, took her brace of pistols and once more demanded to see Jenkins. On receiving the same answer as before that he was not at home, she told her chairmen to stand by and ordered Jenkins's servant to inform his master that she would stay on his doorstep until he appeared even if she must remain there for a month.

Jenkins, realizing that the Duchess would take no excuse for his absence, came to the door.

'I wish to speak to you! I insist,' she said, 'that you hand over to me certain of the money I deposited with you – in cash. I have to return at once to London and have not sufficient money available for the journey. I must have five hundred pounds which, with what I have by me, will suffice to take me to England.'

'But your Grace –' Jenkins spread his hands in a gesture of prevarication – 'your money and securities are in my strong room. It is impossible to obtain for your Grace so large a sum at such short notice.'

'Such short notice be damned! If you do not give me what I insist I must have and that you hold as my banker – a fine honest banker! A crook, an usurer – I will go straight to the British Ambassador and report you.'

'But your Grace –'

'Don't keep me standing here on your doorstep. Let me into your house, or else,' she produced her brace of pistols, 'I will have my money or – your life!'

Jenkins was now thoroughly alarmed, less on account of her threat to report him to the British Ambassador than at the sight of the two pistols levelled directly at his chest. It was evident that the lady knew how to use them. Daring no longer to resist, he admitted her into his house.

'Come into my parlour,' she jeered at him when conducted to an elaborately furnished salon. 'But I'm not your fly. I'm a wasp and these –' she flourished her pistols – 'are my stings. Give me five hundred pounds in coin, no bills to be dishonoured, also my diamond necklace –' she read from a list she had brought with her certain other items of jewellery. 'These I shall require if I remain in England for any length of time. For the rest, as I do not wish to travel with too many valuables, one of my servants will call for those that I leave with you. And if you do not comply with my written order, he will have you arrested at the command of the British Ambassador who will have been acquainted with your refusal to render up my property. And then where will you be?'

Jenkins, now in a pitiable fright, could have guessed where he would be, in a prison cell in Rome and deported to England with what awful consequence he feared to contemplate.

'I beg your Ger-grace', he stammered, 'not to misunderstand me. For the safety of my clients' property I keep all
valuables and money deposited in my – my charge stored
away in –'

'Don't waste your breath while you still have some left
in your body! Go fetch what I must have now. Or –'
again the pistols were pointed. And Jenkins left or rather
bolted from the room.

Elizabeth ensconced herself in a seat and surveyed her
surroundings. Jenkins had obviously made good use of his
clients' deposits, for the salon was sumptuously furnished
with objets d'art and priceless antiques and pictures by
famous artists, past and present.

'God's truth,' muttered Jenkins as he took himself down
to his strong room and extracted from the safe, which was
labelled with the name of the Duchess of Kingston, the
monies and jewels she demanded. 'She is rightly named
Elizabeth. She might be the very spit of England's Queen
whose commands could only be disobeyed under pain of
imprisonment – or worse!'

She had gained her ends and, so far, so good. But there
was no time to be lost before she must leave for England.
She left a few of her most trustworthy servants at the
palace, hustled her men to arrange all travelling conditions, ordered her coach and horses, and without waiting
to make her farewells to her friends in Rome, she started
off on her return journey.

Although she had presented a bold front to Jenkins and
obtained at pistol point all she required, she could not but
review her situation with the utmost misgivings. If, as she
fully realized, Medows were bent on proving her marriage
with Hervey to be valid, then she would be tried for
bigamy as a – felon! Nor did she know that her rank, if
proved she were Kingston's widow and a peeress, could
save her from a felon's fate. But, supposing Medows
should succeed in his attempt to have her charged as a
bigamist, if that treacherous Anne Craddock should be

prevailed upon to come forward as witness to that marriage, which was no marriage, to Hervey, then she saw herself landing at Dover, seized by an officer with a warrant for her arrest, cast into prison there to remain for months before the legal process of the law could bring about a trial. For perjury? Bigamy? Felony? – or what?

She knew that if proven the unlawful wife of Kingston, no privilege of rank could be accorded her and that if found guilty she must be branded – that is burnt in the hand, which was the brutal method of punishment for felony. Horror heaped on horror as she bumped and jolted in the coach on the arduous journey across the Alps and visualized the consequence of Medows' Machiavellian schemes working against her.

Although neither her courage nor her determination to fight to its direful end whatever lay in store for her failed, the execrable roads and the awful bug-ridden inns, and often no inn at all where she could stay for even one night, only a shelter without door or windows where no bed was offered and one must sleep on straw if sleep at all, drained her physical strength. All along the way the ill-kept roads were deeply rutted and filled with stones that caused continuous jolting painfully to bruise her. Her own horses were unused to mountainous roads hewn out of rock, and as they crossed Italy over the Alps down into France the horses sank knee deep in snow, for autumn had sped into winter and to continue by coach was impossible. They halted at the first village, situated at what seemed to be an immeasurable height and the path to it so narrow the wheels of the coach and the horses' hooves looked to be on the edge of a precipice that one false step would hurl all to their deaths.

The inn here in Switzerland was, to Elizabeth's thankfulness, scrupulously clean, the innkeeper offering the best accommodation his wooden chalet could provide, a room for Madame, a bed, soft and downy, and a meal of goat's flesh and such vegetables as could be grown there when the snows had melted. Truly these Swiss, she thought, resting her aching limbs on the first bed she had slept in since she left Rome, are heaven-born. Her servants also were given food and beds if not of down, of sufficient comfort.

When after a night of rest she still suffered great pain from what proved to be an abscess in her side, she asked if a litter could be contrived to carry her on for the remainder of the journey; the coach to follow in gradual stages, her horses to be spared undue hardship. And with two of her men and one borrowed from the innkeeper she was borne in the litter and down into France.

Finally bone-weary, pain-racked, she arrived at Calais where she was received by Dessein, the hotelier, with obsequious homage due to her rank and the promise of rich reward for his service.

There she was got to bed, suffering from a raging fever, and there she stayed for several days until pronounced by the doctor, called to attend her, fit to take the packet to Dover.

Before she left Calais a welcome surprise awaited her in the unexpected arrival of Lord Mansfield, a famous lawyer and an old friend of hers and the Duke's. Having heard from Field that she was on her way back from Rome he had crossed the Channel to meet and reassure her that she had no reason to believe herself in any immediate danger from whatever charge Medows had in mind to indict against her.

And now she, who had been so far removed from news concerning the illness of Bristol, Hervey's brother, during the time she left Rome and her long protracted arrival in England, heard that the Earl of Bristol had died and Hervey had at last succeeded to the Earldom.

'So, my dear,' the old lawyer told her, 'whichever way this case should go, you are still a peeress and will be allowed every courtesy and privilege to which you are entitled.'

'But suppose –' the fear still haunted her that even if a peeress she could be burnt in the hand as a felon – 'should Medows win his case. What then?' She glanced down at her hand and held it palm outward to him. 'Will I suffer this – to be tortured?'

'No, never,' he stoutly denied it. 'You have the law behind you.'

A gleam of laughter shone in her eyes born of relief from awful apprehension. 'I have heard that Walpole who never ceases to stab at me, has for once shown himself inclined to deride the law that would have me in prison tried as a felon, for he calls the law a horrid liar. With all due respect to you, my good lord.'

He took the hand she held out to him and bent his bewigged head to kiss its palm.

'If any lies are to be told, horrid though they may be, they will be told by all of us in support of you, your Grace or – my lady, the Countess of Bristol.'

When, accompanied by Lord Mansfield, she arrived at
Kingston House where he left her in charge of her servants, the buoyant hopes that had sustained her across
the Channel to Dover and thence to Knightsbridge were
shattered by another devastating shock. This was nothing
to do with her case. She might have suffered less to learn
that Medows had already done his worst. No, this was a
personal loss, an added sorrow to her perpetual grief
though she had striven for diversion in the hectically
extravagant life she had led for the past year abroad.

Received by the steward and on asking that her maid
Elizabeth should be sent to her he hesitated before answer-
ing:

'Has not your Grace been informed of . . .'

'Of what?' Whitening fear struck at her. 'What of –
where is Elizabeth?'

'Your Grace,' the man bowed his head. 'I regret to tell
your Grace that she was taken with what Dr Rains called
a hemmer – a bleeding of the lungs.'

'A haemorrhage?' Her stiffened lips framed the word
knowing she pronounced her favourite's death sentence.

'The doctor said, your Grace, it was a galloping con-
sumption.'

'Yes.' Mechanically she accepted it and bade him, 'Tell
Penrose,' another of her women, 'to attend me. I have
been ill and wish to rest.'

Left to herself, her immediate necessities supplied, she
sat by the window that overlooked the gardens which she
had beautified since Kingston House had been her rightful
home. Her thoughts gathered about her in a turmoil of

anger-struck rebellion. Staring down unseeingly at the wintry grounds while the December dusk crept like a ghost drifting along the grassy lawns and the tended paths where gardeners had swept in heaps the fallen leaves ready for the burning. . . . Why, oh why, she cried within her, am I bereft of those few, so very few, I have loved and who have loved me? Just three in all the world, her Evie, the Dowager Princess, yes, she had loved her and her love had been returned, and now . . . this girl, a foster sister whom she had known all her young life, she whom her mother had nurtured . . . gone. Gone where? Oh, the senselessness of it all! The callous indifference of . . . Whom? Who decides our destinies? God? But how can He be a God of love to deprive me of just one, only *one* who could care for me? I have it in me to love if I were allowed to hold and keep and cherish even one of these three. . . . Perhaps it is that I have asked too much.

So did she lash herself and for the first time faced the fact that she had idolized false gods. . . . 'I have lost the Word made Flesh.' She spoke aloud. The sound of her voice in that quiet room roused her to a near frenzy of self-flagellation. Lost to God in the worship of her own miserable creature's desires . . . No! Not desires. Greed. The greed for possessions, of power, of wealth. She had all that. And what was left to her? Disgrace. Your *Grace!* A mirthless laugh escaped her. But she would have loved him had he not been a Duke, as she would have loved Hamilton who failed her, or did he? Was she not then the victim of treachery as now? Anne Craddock. She . . .

'Yes?'

A knock at her door. Penrose, her maid, curtsying to tell her:

'Your Grace, their Graces, the Dukes of Ancaster and Portland have called to know if your Grace will receive them.'

Ancaster, her one-time suitor, her childhood's playmate and Portland, an old friend of her late husband.

206

'Indeed I will see them. Beg their Graces to await me in the drawing-room. Tell Williams and then come back and dress me.'

The fatigue of her journey and the ache of this most recent loss retreated in an upsurge of gratitude that these two who had known her in her heyday had come to her when she believed herself forsaken.

While her women robed her in one of the gowns she had not taken with her to Italy and arranged her hair, she bade them, 'Leave me natural. I detest these pyramidal "heads" that hide what nature gives us.'

Her hair, still a warm brown, was thick and curling with scarce a thread of silver in it as on the day when Pulteney had come upon her in a Devonshire lane; her skin did not require the hare's foot she lightly applied to her cheeks, for she did not want to look, she told her women, 'like a haggish corpse'.

'Your Grace is always lovely, fresh and young as ever,' was the rhapsodized insincere chorus.

'Oil your tongues with honey,' she said turning on them sharply, 'and lace them with vinegar to poke at me behind my back. Fasten my necklace – the pearls. These.' She took them from her jewel case. 'I am in no mood for diamonds.'

'Pearls are for tears, your Grace,' ventured Penrose, a pert comely girl, 'so they say.'

'And as you would wish, but I have shed all the tears that are in me. My fount has run dry.'

But there was still a suspicious brightening of her eyes when she greeted Ancaster and Portland.

'My good dear friends to come to me when I thought myself forgotten. Spurned.'

'Forgotten? Never!' Ancaster who had wooed and not won her bowed over her hand. 'And if spurned, only by those who are not worthy to tie the latchet of your shoe!'

Nor were these two the only men who rallied round

her. The Duke of Newcastle and Lord Mountstuart, the latter whom she hardly knew, supported her, all men, not one woman to stand by her.

She found she could be granted bail preceding the indictment; the Medows family had meanwhile made it clear they would also prosecute the new Lord Bristol for the whole receipt of the Kingston estate. This the latest from Walpole, gleefully scribbling to all and sundry:

'The Earl seems to act on resolution of being divorced; and the Ecclesiastical Court who is as great a whore as either of them affects to be ashamed and thunders against the Duchess. . . .'

But with Lord Mansfield, the Duke of Newcastle and Lord Mountstuart volunteering to stand security for her with others including her neighbour, the Marquis of Granby, whose estate marched with hers at Knightsbridge, she was strengthened to meet her ordeal.

She could shrug away with laughter the malicious humour of Walpole, and the gossip of drawing-rooms where women gathered to gloat upon and prophesy that she 'who calls herself Duchess will be burned in the hand for felony – a bigamist and none other than the wife of Bristol whom she married as Hervey.'

Some of those who spat their spite at her were the wives of the men, Newcastle, Mountstuart, even the old lawyer Mansfield to champion her cause.

'How does she do it?' This from Elizabeth Wortley Montagu, née Ashe, back from Bath. 'To be in at the death!' she tittered. 'How does she have all the men at her feet, even in their dotage or their youth?'

One might well ask why? Not her mere physical attraction. There were many women possessed of more beauty than hers. It is possible that half her charm lay in her readiness sympathetically to hear their confidential indiscretions. It was just this, her keen observance and tolerance of the frailties of both men and women while aware of but not so tolerant of her own. Men appreciated and

208

were encouraged by her interest in them personally rather than for their material advantages. And although she made no secret of her reverence for rank, her innate honesty and ingenuity equated their desire with respect. It was just this in her which women recognized and could not simulate that made her the butt of their enmity.

Neither could Mary Coke nor Mrs Delaney who had dug their claws in 'the Chudleigh' from her first appearance as Maid of Honour, any more than could Walpole, disregard her courage while never giving her that much credit for it.

Armed to meet and combat her present danger that might not only ruin the name she bore and believed to be her lawful right, but also, if judgement opposed her, she could be threatened with the penalty of torture; burnt in the hand as a felon, Mansfield's reassurance notwithstanding. . . . So she waited, prepared to face and fight to their bitterest ends the thundering forces against her. She knew she had a strong support and not a day passed without consultations in her drawing-room that had become a library of law books which she assiduously studied and discussed, driving with her advocates from Knightsbridge to the Temple, Lincoln's Inn and back and forth to Doctors' Commons. The opinions of her counsel gave her much to hope in their decision that the judgement of the Doctors' Commons was irrevocable. The clergy likewise declared conviction impossible. The suit of jactitation had pronounced her marriage with Hervey (Lord Bristol) invalid.

With these assurances that her acquittal would be certain, Elizabeth's anxieties were soothed, and her adamantine resolution to proceed with her defence went apace. Then, one day, there came to her an unexpected and unwelcome visitor, none other than Hervey, Earl of Bristol.

Before she had time to have him dismissed when her footman brought her his card, Hervey as once before forestalled her servant – the black page as it then had been – and was in her room.

There he stood, his face masking the doubt of his reception and with as bold a front as he could present he bowed and, arresting her order to the footman to show his lordship to his carriage which was on her lips unuttered, he said:

'I can only submit my most humble apology for thus intruding on your – your ladyship, for I have to tell that which in *your* interest, not mine, must be told.'

She returned his steady look with one as steady, while her mind misgave her of his intent as to her interest. She saw that the years had dealt lightly with him; although she knew him to be middle-aged, his figure was still upright, his eyes, the keen grey eyes of a sailor as she had known him and as he had first attracted her – so long ago. Another life. Another world.

'What have you to tell that must be told and which I cannot believe is in *my* interest?'

They were both standing. She motioned him to be seated. He said, without a moment's hesitation:

'You are, I understand, acquainted with a woman who has been in the service of your late aunt, Mrs Hanmer – one Anne Craddock as she calls herself, but she married a servant of mine whom I am told is dead and now reverts to her maiden name?'

'Yes, I was acquainted with that woman many years ago. What of it?'

'This is what of it.' He crossed one white-silk-stockinged knee over the other. 'She has approached me whom I have not seen since I dismissed her husband for dishonesty.'

'Why did she approach you? For the same reason, I presume, that she has recently approached me?'

'If to extract money from you to keep her silence that she can produce evidence of our marriage, I can answer you – yes. She informed me that you bore me a son who died in his infancy. You did not let me know of this.'

'Why should I have let you know? That son was born of rape. Our marriage has been proven null and void. The case which is to be brought against me for bigamously marrying the Duke of Kingston, my one and only lawful husband, will be dismissed and I acquitted. There is no evidence of our marriage other than this woman's word which is blackmail to extort money from me on false pretences. All those who witnessed that improbable and illegal wedding at midnight are dead and there is no certificate of the marriage.'

'That,' he imperturbably replied, 'is so far as I did understand, and no witness more than this woman Craddock who threatens you and one other – the wife and widow of the clergyman who performed what you call an improbable and illegal wedding. As to no certificate of the marriage, this woman Craddock is prepared to swear that the clergyman's widow who was remarried to your – the late Duke's butler, has the original certificate in her keeping.'

'No!' She started up. 'There is no certificate. I saw –' she stopped, seeing his eyebrows elevated and on his lips a question to prompt:

'You saw?'

Should she confess to him? Would it be better to keep her visit to Lainston a secret with the destruction of the leaf she had torn from the register? What was in his mind? Was he friend or foe? And as if he read her thoughts he said with slow deliberation, 'You may think ill of me, as you have every right to think, but I am here on your behalf. If you go through with this defence against a bigamous marriage with Kingston you will suffer – you are bound to suffer a conviction of your guilt. But if you do not defend, which is an admission that you and I are husband and wife – *legally* husband and wife – and that you in all innocence believed our marriage to have been no marriage in that it was never consummated, I am prepared to swear that I and I alone am to blame. I took an oath in the Ecclesiastical Court that I was eighteen and, you too, a minor. You were not a minor but I was. Not eighteen, that was a lie, but it was not a lie to swear myself a minor. I was not twenty and I told you and let you believe I was twenty-two. The case can be heard in chambers and you will be found guilty but unwittingly of bigamy and therefore innocent and acquitted.'

She was silent to consider the significance of his offer for which she could be saved the felonious charge against her. And then – what then? Would she be Hervey's wife and not Kingston's widow? Her marriage to *him* null and void, as had been proved was her marriage to Hervey? Or, if the verdict of the Ecclesiastical Court were to be disproved and she pronounced the wife of Hervey, now Earl of Bristol, he could bring an action against her for divorce on the grounds of adultery. Or again, were she to agree not to defend the charge of bigamy having in all innocence married Kingston, then Hervey would have the right to claim her as his wife, forgo divorce proceedings against the dead Duke, and take whatever consequences would ensue from his perjured evidence which, after all, was only a question of falsifying her age as a minor, not *his* age, if in truth he had been under twenty-one. . . .

'Good God!' She passed a hand across her forehead. 'I am so utterly bemused – I cannot think – I'm all at sea. Are you aware, as I am told by Lord Mansfield, that the Medows family not only wish to dispossess me of my husband's Will but intend to prosecute you for the whole of the Kingston estate if our marriage is proved to be legal, and I am your Countess? Did you know of this?'

'I did – and I do, and I am prepared to forfeit all right, if any such right there be, to the Kingston estate since you are my wife and not his widow.'

'Why – why in God's or the devil's name –' she had not reseated herself although he remained where he was sitting, his legs uncrossed and leaning forward on the settee – 'why involve yourself in all this revolting case against me? What devilry lies behind your suggestion? What do you gain from it?' She stood before him, her hands clenched at her sides, her face blanched, not with fear, with accusative suspicion.

He answered her quietly with the one word:

'Atonement.'

She drew in a long breath.

'So, you realize how I have suffered and did suffer from your abuse of what you called your marital privilege? You have the grace to admit how you wronged me?'

His head in his hands, his voice came to her muffled. 'Do you think I have not suffered too?'

'Yet you wished to divorce me, make me an adulteress believing we were married – man and wife? So that you could wed a girl you fancied and degrade her as you defiled and degraded me? Her father must have known of your – your propensities for I hear he paid five thousand pounds to her that she should refuse you.'

He sprang to his feet.

'I can offer no excuse for what in my youth – denied for months, no, years sometimes, the sight of women, that I and others sank to, which you regard and I admit was degradation. I have fought sea battles for my King and country, have risked my life and willingly in the service that has been for me more than the love of or desire for a woman, but even now, after all these many years, I still desire you as my woman and – my wife. And –' his voice dwindled, she hardly heard him say 'I want an heir.'

Her hands unclenched; she spread them palm upwards in a helpless gesture.

'Are you mad? Yes, you are, you have always been mad. Abnormal. I am nearing fifty.'

'You have borne me a son who would have been my heir. You are still of child-bearing age according to the law. I have studied it to find that the maximum legal age of child-bearing is fifty-one. If I have no son then my brother, the Bishop of Derry, is my heir. I want your son – *our* son to replace him whom I have lost.'

'Anne Craddock has told you all she knows or thinks she knows of me and the birth of that son, born of rape?'

'There is no rape between man and wife in the consummation of a marriage.'

'How you harp on that misplaced assumption. We were never and are not and can *never* be man and wife. What lies behind this –' her lip curled disgustedly – 'sacrificial chivalry I cannot guess, but that it suits your purpose for some reason which is obscure to me, is nothing to *my* purpose, that is certain. No, Hervey,' as he made as if to take her hands with the hot denial – 'You wrong me. I swear –'

'Don't swear to more lies or excuses, or to an atonement. There is no atonement for that which you did and have done to me, except to free me from the bondage of your name that I could live in the love of a man of honour who, had he been a ploughman or a pauper I would have been proud to have been his wife as I am proud, though grieved, to be his widow. No, Hervey – Bristol, as I suppose you are now – I will go through with my defence. It is as my lawyers assure me a strong defence. I have,' a small smile hovered at the corners of her desirable mouth, 'something in the nature of a thunderbolt in preparation for my lords for I insist on being tried by my peers!'

'Your peers? How?' Again he approached her, and again she backed from him. 'If you deny our marriage you are no peeress. Do you think the House of Lords who would charge you for bigamy will grant you the right to name yourself Kingston's Duchess? You would be tried as a commoner – a felon.'

'I am no commoner and no felon.' She reared her head pronouncing her defiance. 'I am a peeress – and I am that I *am*!'

'You have a proud conceit of yourself,' half admiringly, half jestingly he spoke, 'to quote God's Word for *Him*self as applicable to you!'

'Conceit? No. Faith in right and justice, yes! I will be my own Counsel and conduct my own defence.' And as he would have spoken she pointed to the door. 'Go. Leave me. Do your worst or, if you think to do your best for me I'll have none of you.' She moved to the bell-rope.

'Do not summon your servant to show me out. You have answered me, as you would say, in right and justice. This being so, I abide by your decision and – I take my leave.'

He bowed, turned, and without another word or backward look he went.

Long after he had gone she stayed. Dusk was falling on the April day. A footman came to light the candles. She bade him: 'No, I will ring when I wish for lights.'

She sat in the window-seat watching the sky turn from its springtime opalescence to a darkening gauze-like curtain, herald of the rising moon. One vivid star shone out, the evening star. . . . My star. She wondered, are the stars for or against me?

Perusing in her mind, not without compunction, her refusal to accept what Hervey believed to be in her sole interest by his offer to commit himself on her behalf and to gain thereby – what? At the worst indictment for perjury, which was no perjury if, as now she realized, he were indeed a minor when they went through a form of marriage, or at the best – for him, to prove himself her husband and so to claim her. Had she dealt too hardly with him? Was he really intending atonement? Prepared, for her sake, to save her the shame of the charge against her and to prove himself her lawful husband, and if so proved, to be prosecuted by the Medows family for the whole receipt of the Kingston estate, willed to Kingston's widow who had not been Kingston's wife. . . . But how could this be?

She found no answer in her search of the stars that one by one sparked through the slow candescence of the young crescent moon lying on her back above the tree tops in the gardens – *her* gardens of *her* house! Kingston House, willed to her by her one and only husband . . .

'My God!' she apostrophized the heavens, shaking a fist as if in the face of all the judges and the Medows who would reprive her of what was hers by deed and Will and lawful marriage. 'I swear I'll fight and win if it takes the last drop of my blood and be damned to you all who seek to wrong me! Not you, Hervey. I believe you wish me well and take your word for it, but not to act on it. I stand by *my* word, and my word alone! . . .'

*   *   *

She was not alone although she had been quite ready to have fought her battle unaided except for the advice of her attorney, Field, in whom she had less faith than in her own judgement, and persistent belief that she was Kingston's lawful widow. While she remained satisfied that her acquittal was certain, she proceeded with her petition after interminable consultations with her legal advisers for the removal of the bill of indictment and the presentment signed by the grand jurors on the grounds that the Lords proposed to try her as a commoner and not as a peeress as she claimed to be.

That she should be styled as Elizabeth Hervey instead of the title to which she laid claim as the Duchess of Kingston, drove her to a frenzy of wrath and increased her determination never to budge one iota from that which she firmly believed to be due to her lawful rank. The peers were now placed in an unprecedented situation. If they consented to her petition, they must admit she had every right to claim herself a Duchess and to be tried in the Court of the King's Bench and would certainly have pleaded privilege and, as no judge would have ventured to have opposed that right, the trial could not have proceeded. According to Lord Mansfield there was a third course to pursue – 'They might,' he told her, 'refer the claim to the Attorney-General and the Solicitor-General and they would then proceed on the Ecclesiastical decision, and the registration of your marriage to the Duke of Kingston would finally prove your claim to be the Duchess of Kingston.'

'Then why,' she demanded, 'all this dilly-dallying? Let them admit the marriage legal and so put an end to this disgraceful persecution.'

'Because,' the old lawyer took snuff and, inhaling the spicy bergamot, said with a twinkle: 'The Lords find themselves on the horns of a dilemma. Having gone to such pains to help Medows whom they are convinced is in the right to dispute his uncle's Will, assuming you were the late Duke's mistress and not his wife, they must proceed in a series of complications that can only make themselves look ridiculous and land the country in vast expense to prove nothing. And if they insist that you are *not* a widowed Duchess guilty of bigamy, you are still a peeress, wife of the Earl of Bristol, and can be tried as such.'

'The whole thing,' Elizabeth's sense of humour never failed her even when calamity threatened, 'is developing into a farce. How will they indict me? As the Duchess of Kingston by the name of Elizabeth Chudleigh, Countess and wife of August Hervey, now Earl of Bristol? And will you, my lord, be one of my jurors when I stand at the bar in the House of Lords?'

'If it were possible,' the twinkle developed into a chuckle, 'which it is not, for only a selected number of peers can stand to judge you which I could not as your legal adviser. You would be acquitted instantly by my one voice alone were I to be one of your jurors. But have no fear. Whether you be tried as a commoner or peeress, you will be acquitted. I give you my word for it.'

And on his word for it she waited with the heavy load

217

of doubt and apprehension lifted, while the law lords debated and blundered through endless arguments as to whether the lady had the right to be tried as a peeress or as the wife of a commoner as she was when married to Augustus Hervey. Or if not the widow of the Duke of Kingston, for they must prove beyond doubt she had never been *his* wife, and since an earldom had devolved upon Augustus Hervey it must be confirmed, were she proven a bigamist even if the wife of Lord Bristol, a peer, and so be tried as such.

'They are surely run mad as the inmates of Bethlem,' laughed Elizabeth to her attorney, Field. 'Such a set of lunatics to sit in judgement on me can only mean that I'm acquitted before I'm tried.'

Field was not so inclined to laughter; only a thin smile came upon his close pressed lips before he replied:

'We must always be prepared for the predictable rather than the unpredictable.'

'I can predict with certainty for I shall conduct my own case.'

A look of dismay mounting to horror overspread the lawyer's face. His chin quivered. 'Your Grace! I have briefed the two most eminent Counsel in the country to undertake your defence. But you must be aware that the onus of defence as it is now, which we of the law hope to see altered, rests upon the prisoner alone. Only he, or she –' he bent his head – 'can address the Lords in your defence.'

'All the same, I, the prisoner (how awful it sounds!), can write my address and read it and, or, add to it extempore. I am accustomed to extemporize. In my years at Court I have learned the art of impromptu *and* dissimulation. I can hardly wait for the great day!'

But she had to wait. And it did nothing to curb her impatience when there came from another quarter a disturbance as if a gale had arisen to swell the placid waters of her faith in her ultimate success.

This had no connection with her present pending case. It came from a favourite of the playhouse, a comedian, popular both with men and, particularly, women of fashion. He was a great mimic and induced roars of laughter by his apt and recognizable imitations of well-known personages. His voice and gestures unmistakably rendered, sometimes with some amusingly malicious intent were it of a famous politician representing the party of either Government, always went down well whether in or out of favour. His caricatures did not usually run to a whole comedy but on occasion he would stage a play in which the characters were obviously meant to portray persons of consequence.

Whether or not this Samuel Foote had any thought of exacting blackmail by introducing the Duchess of Kingston into a new comedy entitled *A Trip to Calais* which was the general opinion at the time, is uncertain. But that Foote should have chosen to fix upon Calais, where it was known the Duchess on her hurried return from Rome lay ill of a fever for several days, might, as Foote averred, have been coincidental. Yet his denial that he had any intention of associating the Duchess with his leading lady, whom he named 'Lady Kitty Crocodile', a deliberate jibe at the outward show of grief and the tears of the Duchess at her husband's death, was only one of his many thrusts at her; another being a marked reference to Iphigenia which half London remembered from that unforgotten masquerade.

There were various other identifications including 'two husbands and a sixteen years' siege of resistance between the marriage of the first husband whom Lady Kitty married in 1744, and her second marriage in 1769', the date of the wedding to Kingston. These correct dates of both weddings to 'the two husbands' and Lady Kitty's advice to one of her maids, described as her 'Maids of Honour' which Elizabeth used jestingly to call them, indubitably confirmed who 'Lady Kitty' was meant to be.

'Suppose,' says Lady Kitty to her maid to help her choice between two lovers, 'that you marry both of them?'

Whatever Foote's denial that he had no intent whatsoever of 'pillorying' the Duchess, as she declared, when the news came to her that Foote had arranged to present the play at the Haymarket Playhouse, Elizabeth demanded that a copy of the play should be sent to her. It had already reached her ears how Foote had made her his butt in the character of 'Lady Kitty Crocodile', but on second thoughts and before she would take legal advice, and rather than have a copy of the play sent to her which might have been deliberately cut of any libellous content, she ordered Foote to attend her with the play and to read it to her in its entirety.

To make sure that he would not omit anything that referred to herself, she looked through each page before she made him sit and read every word of it.

When he came to the scenes in which her obvious counterpart figured, she who had held herself in now let herself out.

Tearing the script from his hands, she read the scene that so derided her and as her fury mounted, she fell into a passion of rage in which she hurled at him a volley of abuse.

This did not in the least dismay him whose risible faculties under control simulated gravity, for the more she stormed the more he knew that his comedy depicting Lady Kitty as a virago would gain him his ends – namely to extort from the Duchess a considerable sum of money not to produce the play on the stage or – he would make this an extra stipulation – never to allow his play to be published.

Assuming an air of the most injured innocence he begged her Grace to believe his word, on oath if need be, that not any one character, in especial that of Lady Kitty

Crocodile, was intended for and could be traced to her Grace nor to anyone of her attendants or associates.

But this endeavour to make her see reason served only to make her see red.

'You scoundrelly liar! Every word this creature you portray in my likeness is as near as possible to my own shreds of conversation with my women. You must have been sneaking around, offering free tickets for your clownish performances, and more than tickets I'll be bound. Why, the very name you give to one of this "Lady Kitty's" maids, "Pomose", is a thin disguise for my woman Penrose whom I have dismissed for insolence.'

While he made attempt again to assure her that whatever construction she chose to attribute to her Grace's self was entirely erroneous, she did some rapid thinking.

Sketching on her face the semblance of a conciliatory smile she feigned capitulation.

'I have always enjoyed your inimitable comedies and imitations even of the recent Prime Minister whom I have seen shaking with laughter at your mimicry of him. If you will allow me to retain the script of your play I promise to return it to you tomorrow without fail.'

Foote, who had a faithful copy of the script, agreed to allow her request.

She took it from him and sent him away well satisfied that he held the trump card to the tune of two thousand pounds which he would demand as the price of his withdrawal of his production of the play. But she too held a trump card – up her sleeve.

When the next morning Foote arrived to reclaim his play, she asked him to name his price for the copyright of his 'satire' as she called it. He named his price. 'Two thousand pounds, your Grace, which will not compensate me for the loss I shall sustain in not producing this little comedy. But to oblige your Grace –'

'No, you disoblige me at such an exorbitant sum for your hush-money. No, and no again! I have a draft waiting for my signature at my bank for sixteen hundred pounds to be paid to you for the rights of your libellous representation of myself.'

She made the offer knowing perfectly well he would refuse it and demand not a penny less than the two thousand pounds – 'which as a favour to your estimable Grace, I will accept for the purchase of my play, the rights to revert to yourself absolutely.'

'You'll get not a penny more from me than the sixteen hundred pounds I have waiting for my signature to save you from a case of libel.'

'There is no libel, your Grace, in any word of my play than can be proved against me as levelled at you.'

'That remains to be seen,' said she. 'Take your false envenomed rubbish and produce it at the Haymarket Playhouse at your peril.'

'*My* peril, madam?' he had the impudence to reply. 'You cannot, surely, with so serious a case as that of bigamy to be tried and judged against you, compare your peril to mine!'

With which he bowed and left her. Nothing he could have said or done could have placed him in a worse position than this allusion to the case in which all London knew she would shortly be involved, tried, and judged as a felon, though none but Hervey knew – she had not yet told her lawyer, Field – that she would insist she be tried by her peers, nor that two Dukes and an Earl were standing security for her.

Foote, stung with disappointment to secure the money far in advance of that which the proceeds of his play, should he present it, would earn him, made a supreme effort to obtain a licence for the production from the Lord Chamberlain.

Meanwhile Elizabeth had consulted her good friend, the Duke of Newcastle, on whose advice she took Counsel's opinion. Before returning the manuscript, she had taken the precaution of copying each sentence of the play in

222

every page that related to herself and her associates before she returned it to Foote. She sat up all night until dawn, carefully copying any word that could be construed as libellous.

The opinion of Counsel, of her lawyer Field, and a journalistic parson, the Rev. Mr Jackson, all recommended by Newcastle, were unanimous in pronouncing the comedy as a false, gross and malicious libel. They strongly advised her not to give one guinea to Foote. Mr Jackson, who had much influence with the newspapers, suggested instead of complying with Foote's outrageous demand, that:

'Your Grace should consult Mr Field as to the advisability of prosecuting Foote for his endeavour to extort money from you by threats amounting to blackmail.'

The Committee unanimously agreed to this proposition and Jackson at once went to tell Foote that the Duchess had sworn not to allow him a single guinea. Foote having at first hummed and hahed, and although well aware of Jackson's influence with the press and, as a Privy Councillor, with the Law Lords, he finally decided that he would go ahead with the production of the play.

Shedding all pretence at compromise he shouted: 'I am determined to publish the piece unless the Duchess will compensate me for the loss which I will sustain if I withdraw it. Why should you, sir, or anyone else interfere with a matter that is entirely between her Grace and myself? The part of Lady Kitty Crocodile will suit nine out of ten widows of quality in the Kingdom. As for the allusion to their tears, they are like a shower in sunshine refreshing their weeds!'

'If that is your decision,' Jackson gave him a meaningful look, 'I wish you good morning.'

Foote strode up to him as he went to the door. 'What the devil,' he demanded, 'do you think you and your Grub Street scribblers can do to prevent my production of a

223

comedy that has no connection whatsoever with the Duchess or any identifiable person? Am I to be attacked if I publish *A Trip to Calais*?'

'The publication,' was Jackson's cool reply, 'will be an attack from *you*, Mr Foote, which I as a friend of the Duchess will do my utmost to prevent.'

Foote now found himself between the devil of a Duchess and the printers' ink blue sea. That Jackson could and would attack him through the news-sheets which might damage him far more than the loss of his hush-money to withdraw his play, gave him furiously to think. . . . 'A friend of the Duchess!' Yes, and of the Lord Chamberlain who had made no reply to his appeal. When again he approached, in all humility, the Lord Chamberlain with a lengthy epistle, flowery with verbiage in which 'Your Lordship will, I doubt not, permit me to enjoy the fruits of my labour because a capricious individual has taken it into her head that I have pinned her ruffle awry.' (What exactly he meant by her ruffle, unless an allusion to the neckwear she favoured which resembled that worn by the greatest of Elizabeths, Queen, is uncertain) but he goes on to ask: 'Why should I be punished by a poniard struck deep in my heart? Your Lordship's determination is of greatest importance to me now, and must inevitably decide my fate. Between the muse and the magistrate there is a natural affinity.'

A somewhat tactless parallel to draw between a comedian playactor and playwright and the great Lord Chamberlain, Earl of Hertford. This put the final prohibition on the performance of his play. The Chamberlain definitely refused to grant Foote his desired licence. Hertford, who had often enjoyed the wit and humour of Foote's imitations, saw neither wit nor humour in what amounted to a demand with intent to rob as from a highwayman, who, as the Chamberlain reported: 'Instead of pointing a pistol at the lady he substitutes a libel saying, "Your money or I'll destroy your reputation!"'

Foote now realized the game was up and that he had lost not only the compensation he had attempted to extort for the withdrawal of his play but he must face the sniggers of the newsprints at his expense, and of all things he feared the greatest was adverse publicity. The Duchess, always hot news for Grub Street, was the particular prey of prowling reporters. They had their pens ready now to pounce on her name which the Walpole and Coke contingent bandied in letters and defamatory talk. So Foote, dreading a newspaper war, wrote what he hoped to be a conciliatory letter to:

Her Grace the Duchess of Kingston
Madam,
A member of the Privy Council and a friend of your Grace's – he has begged me not to mention his name but your Grace will easily guess who – [Jackson, of course] has explained to me what I did not conceive that the publication of the scenes in *A Trip to Calais* might be of infinite ill-consequence to your affairs. [A sly dig at her forthcoming trial.] I therefore give up to that consideration what neither your Grace's offers nor the threats of your agents could obtain. The scenes shall not be published nor shall anything appear in my theatre from me that can hurt you provided that the attacks made on me in the newspapers do not make it necessary for me to act in defence of myself. . . .
    I have the honour to be,
                            Your Grace's most devoted servant,
                            Samuel Foote.

This is where Elizabeth made a fatal mistake. Had she rested on her laurels for having thwarted Foote's blackmailing intent, it would have finished what appears to have been much ado about nothing. But finding from his letter that he went in fear of attack from the press, she insisted that Jackson should have Foote's letter printed along with her reply to it.

In vain did the parson journalist argue with her concerning the impropriety of a newspaper contest as beneath her dignity. Secure in her triumph that augured well for her eventual conquest if or when brought to trial for alleged bigamy, she sharpened her wit with her quill and returned Foote's letter with one of much length and extravagant abuse to this effect:

> Kingston House
> August 13th

Sir,

I was at dinner when I received your ill-judged letter. As there is little consideration required, I shall sacrifice a few moments to answer it. [The few moments lengthened to an hour before she had re-written and corrected it to her satisfaction.] . . . If I abhorred you for your slander, I now despise you for your concessions. It is proof of the illiberality of your satire when you can publish or suppress it as best suits the needy convenience of your purse. You first had the cowardly business to draw the sword; and if I sheath it until I make you crouch like the subservient vassal you are, then there is no spirit in an injured woman or meanness in a slanderous buffoon.

This was bad enough, but not content with that she needs must heap insult upon injury with no thought of the consequence, nor how the news-sheets would seize upon this attack from her which, however much it might mortify Foote, would put him in a strong position should he publish the Duchess's letter in reply to his.

> Clothed in my innocence as in a coat of mail I am proof against a host of foes . . . I scorn to be bullied into a purchase of your silence.

She ends with as flowery an attempt at sarcasm as any satirical travesty Foote could have improvised.

226

I will keep the pity [his concessions?] you send until the morning when I will return it with a box of lip salve; and a choir of choristers shall chant a stave to your requiem.

E. Kingston

Foote's reply to this letter was in much the same vein with the added experience of a professional writer. At once the journalistic choristers began to chant, not the requiem to Foote with which Elizabeth had taunted him, but with a stinging chorus of personal and impersonal letters, some anonymous, and a series of articles that appeared in the press most of which, as Foote was popular with the general public and with Grub Street, plunged everyone who had enjoyed Foote's imitations into the fight as his allies.

Walpole, as might have been expected, was delighted with the furore that *A Trip to Calais*, banned by the Lord Chamberlain, had brought about to involve the Duchess in a paper war.

The cynic of Strawberry Hill gave rein to malicious invention in writing to his friend and chief correspondent, Horace Mann: 'The heroine of Doctors' Commons, the Duchess of Kingston, has at last made her folly, which I have long known, as public as her shame by entering the lists with a merry-andrew who is no fool. . . . Drunk with her own triumph she would give the vital blow with her own hand. But as the instrument she chose was a goose quill the stroke recoiled on herself. She wrote a letter to the *Evening Post*.' (This was in Horace's imagination, for no letter of hers was written to the Press, from which she recoiled as from the poison of a rattlesnake.)

Horace continues, piling it on with his own serpentine brand of venom directed at Elizabeth since their childhood days. 'To which not the lowest of her class who tramps in pattens would set her mark . . . Billingsgate from a ducal coronet was irritating, but Foote with all the delicacy *she* ought to have used, replied only with wit and irony. I imagine she will escape trial but Foote has given her the *coup de grâce*.'

Walpole was mistaken. Elizabeth did not escape trial, though it was not she who received the *coup de grâce* but Foote who, having made a butt of the Duchess and held her up to ridicule, saw it rebound on himself. Nevertheless this unsavoury publicity had its ill-effect on the Duchess as well as upon Foote. She would have done better to rest content with her victory over Foote than to have entered into all that Grub Street correspondence which did neither of them any good and brought the Medows family hot on her scent to encourage her slanderers, preparing to run her to earth.

The wheels of law that hitherto had been revolving slowly now gathered impetus to proceed with the preliminaries of the trial, and the date was appointed for 24 January 1776.

When Lord Mansfield came to tell her the date of her trial at the Court of King's Bench (as more dignified than the Old Bailey), he was admitted to her bedroom. She had taken to her bed. Her face, carefully plastered with rice powder, presented the appearance of a woman in the final stages of decline. Her breathing was difficult, her voice weak as she apologized for receiving him in her bedroom and in such sorry case.

'My poor child! Why did you not let me know of your illness? I can see you are in no fit state to discuss what lies before you.'

'That is so. May I – be granted a delay – before the date is finally decided?' She spoke between pauses, gathering her breath and in so faint a voice he scarce could hear her. 'The law proposes and God – disposes. But, my Lord, have they – the House of Lords – refused to – to grant me my rights as a – peeress?'

'The question,' said Lord Mansfield, 'is still under discussion, but the date of the trial, whether it be in the

House of Lords or before the Justice of the King's Bench, is yet to be decided. . . . My dear, you look so pale, I tire you. I will leave you now. Send for your woman to attend you.'

He bowed himself out and, as the door closed, she flung off the bed clothes and went to her bureau. There she wrote a letter to Field in which she summoned him to call on her at once.

She rang for a footman to deliver it and when he had gone with the note, she burst into laughter, loud and long.

Dear old Mansfield, she inly addressed him, did you not, when I came back from Calais, let me believe I would surely be tried by my peers and now you leave me guessing. Well, you can all go on guessing but I prepare my counterstroke. I'll have the whole lot of you running round in circles. . . .

When Field came in answer to her summons she was still in bed.

'*J'y suis, j'y reste,*' she told him. 'I am ill and I am in no fit state to attend my trial in one month from now. I require more time to prepare my counterbolt and to discharge my batteries in the dumbfounded faces of their lordships. I claim,' she told the flabbergasted Field, 'my right to be tried by – my peers!'

Elizabeth's ultimatum to be tried by her peers in Westminster Hall came as a thunderbolt upon the horrified
Lords. After endless debates and arguments in which it
had been decided that the lady having been indicted as a
commoner, by what legal right could she claim to be a
peeress? She, the wife of Augustus John Hervey (discount-
ing the jurisdiction of the Ecclesiastical Court), therefore
was the lady's own claim to be Kingston's widow of sufficient validity to constitute her a peeress? Or, since a peerage had but recently devolved upon Augustus Hervey,
how could it be certain that the indictment specified the
lady as the wife of that gentleman? The lady, for all that
appeared on the record, might be the wife of any other
commoner of the same Christian and surname as of him
who was now the Earl of Bristol.

It was the Earl of Hillsborough who brought up these
controversies. He reminded the House of Lords that many
years had elapsed since the alleged marriage to the Hon.
Augustus Hervey had taken place, during which time the
marriage of the unhappy lady to the Duke of Kingston
had been formally recognized and her rank universally
admitted. There was so much force in this argument that
scarcely a peer present could not know that the whole
action had been set on foot by the Medows family to
procure evidence against the Duchess and so refute the
Will of the Duke of Kingston that made his 'wife' who,
according to Medows, was *not* his wife but his mistress
and the legatee of the whole of the late Duke's residuary
estate.

It would seem that no sooner had the Lords overcome

one dilemma than they found themselves faced with another. The Duke of Richmond presented the following queries:

'Can the House proceed in the trial of the lady styling herself the Duchess of Kingston by the name of Elizabeth, wife of Augustus Hervey, Esq? And whether, if she could be so tried upon this indictment and found guilty, might she not allege incompetency of jurisdiction?'

To this question the Lords had nothing to say since the great majority of the peers to sit in judgement on 'the lady styling herself the Duchess of Kingston', knew probably less of the law than did 'the lady'. For all these months after her return from Rome Elizabeth had been studying legal books and in continuous conference with Lord Mansfield and her attorney, Field. Therefore the Lords, to be on the safe side, decided with one voice to oppose the Duke of Richmond's proposition; whereupon it was withdrawn. But after further considerable argument and discussion it was finally agreed to add the words 'now Earl of Bristol' after Augustus John Hervey, which, however, would make the lady named as Mrs Hervey 'now Countess of Bristol'.

More consternation and confusion. Tempers were lost, wordy arguments ensued until Lord Lyttelton came across with the bright idea that His Majesty should be approached to appoint a Lord High Steward. This obviously would mean that 'the lady styling herself the Duchess of Kingston, wife of Augustus John Hervey now Earl of Bristol had the right to be tried by her peers'.

Elizabeth, to whom all this was reported by her faithful Lord Mansfield, declared: 'They are naught but a lot of Bedlamites running round in circles and not a man among them knows the most elementary rudiments of the law, especially appertaining to the House of Lords. I'd have stood a better chance before a magistrate.'

Lord Mansfield was inclined to agree with her but refrained from saying so.

Meanwhile the latest problem that presented itself to the harassed Lords was that only two peers in that century had been tried in Westminster Hall: one, the 'mad' Lord Ferrers, found guilty of murder and hanged; the other, Lord Byron, indicted of murder but acquitted. And never, no never! the Lords unanimously agreed, had there been a trial for bigamy brought before them, the accused being a woman and they, their Lordships, sitting in judgement to inquire into the charge against the said Elizabeth Hervey, wife of Augustus Hervey, who on such a day and place did marry the said Augustus John Hervey, and on such a day and place in the parish of St George's Hanover Square did with force of arms marry the said Evelyn, Duke of Kingston the said previous husband being then alive . . . and so on with exhaustless repetition.

'*With force of arms.*' This was too much, even for the Lords, who dissolved into laughter − blessed relief no doubt from the continuous arguments and debates.

Elizabeth, to whom all was fully reported, likewise laughed hysterically, spluttering to Ancaster, who had brought her this latest development:

'Foote himself − could − could not have written a more side-splitting comedy!'

But she saw no comedy in the final decision from the Lord Chancellor that it was impossible to try the lady unless she were in custody. She must be a prisoner before she could be tried.

'I − a prisoner! Good God!' raved Elizabeth when Lord Mansfield brought her the Lord Chancellor's mandate. 'Where am I to be imprisoned? In the Tower? In Newgate? In −'

'It is merely a figure of speech,' she was assured. 'It has been agreed that you will be in the custody of Black Rod.'

'Black Rod!' She burst again into laughter. 'Sir Francis Molyneux! Oh, but this is too rich! Black Rod is, or was,

232

a particular friend of my beloved Duke and I have known him as long as I had known my husband.'

'Which being so and you in the custody of Black Rod, should the trial last more than a day –'

'A day!' she interrupted, 'at the rate the Lords are conducting the preliminaries it looks to last a year!'

'Say two or three days,' Lord Mansfield patiently continued, 'or one day, you may either go to your own home or to apartments arranged by the House to accommodate you. But wherever you may be you would still be in the custody – or shall we suggest – *presumed* to be in the custody of Black Rod.'

At last the matter was settled, the trial to take place on 15 April 1776, after a postponement of four months due to 'the Lady's' (convenient) illness. It seemed that the only title by which she could at present be identified was that of 'the Lady', which was carefully non-committal.

Never had there been such excited interest over a trial, never such an incessant demand for tickets from all strata of society. Although trials in Westminster Hall for peers were not unknown, but few enough, the trial of a peeress was quite without precedent, to give further headaches to the Lords who, before it began, were heartily sick of the whole business and especially of the various names of 'the Lady', or as she must be known at the bar 'the prisoner'. And whether judgement went for or against her would she be rightfully addressed as Elizabeth Kingston, Duchess, or Elizabeth Hervey or, if proven unmarried either to the late Duke or the present Earl of Bristol, would she still be Elizabeth Chudleigh, spinster? None of them could decide on *that*.

Every official who had the smallest influence was besieged by clamorous demands for tickets. Even the foreign ambassadors were pestered by petitioners. Bribes were offered, some accepted by underlings who might be persuaded to provide seats to witness what looked to be the trial of the century.

The only person who appeared to be the least affected was the leading lady in the whole tragi-comedy or, as she insisted on describing it, 'the farce'. She might have shown more anticipatory excitement were she preparing to attend a first night of one of Mr Garrick's performances. He, the greatest actor of his time, graciously offered his ticket to the very proper and pious Hannah More, whose literary works and do-gooding attempts to improve the manners and morals of society made her the least popular among women of fashion but charmed the equally pious Queen Charlotte.

Garrick, who had been a partisan of Elizabeth long before she became the wife of Kingston, could not bring himself to see her brought to trial; but his wife accompanied Hannah More. Her graphic account of the proceedings in which it was apparent she delighted to see the notorious Elizabeth Chudleigh pilloried was, for all its literary merit, prejudicially uncharitable.

Prior to the formal procession of the peers, Queen Charlotte arrived with the Duke of Newcastle in attendance, and the Prince of Wales, the Duke of York (made Bishop of Osnaburgh when he was three years old) and the Princess Royal; the ages of these three royal children had not yet totalled forty. The King had evidently decided not to attend the trial for the same reason as Garrick, for George could not have forgotten his affection for her, now 'the prisoner at the bar'.

At precisely a quarter after eleven o'clock on the first morning of the trial the procession of the Lords assembled in the following manner.

The Lord High Steward's attendants taking precedence, two and two, before the Clerk's Assistant to the House of Lords and the Clerk of Parliament. Then the Clerk of the Crown in the Court of Chancery bearing the King's commission to the Lord High Steward. Then the Masters of Chancery, two and two.

The Judges, two and two.

The eldest sons of the peers came next, two and two, and minor peers, two and two; the Heralds Chester and Somerset, four Serjeants-at-arms and then:

The Barons two and two, beginning with the youngest Baron.

The Bishops, two and two.

Viscounts and other peers, two and two.

The Lord Privy Seal and Lord President.

The Archbishops of York and Canterbury.

Garter King-of-Arms and the Gentleman Usher of the Black Rod.

The Lord Chancellor of Great Britain, and His Grace the Lord High Steward, his train borne; and finally in order of rank the senior peers and the Dukes.

The spectators in the gallery allotted to them began to be bored by this seemingly endless procession, despite the sumptuous array of peers in their scarlet and ermine, their coronets perched precariously on their powdered wigs. When would 'she' be brought in? went the whispers of the women who had come to see 'the Chudleigh', the most talked of, maligned and envied of all who had known or had not known her.

Before the House could resume with its proceedings there was a perpetual to-ing and fro-ing by Garter-King-of-Arms, striving to assemble the peers in their rightful order in the procession. There was continuous re-shuffling on the part of Rouge Dragon, assisting Black Rod who had all to do with his mind on 'the prisoner' in his custody.

'Your Grace,' expostulated the hot and bothered Garter-King-of-Arms, marshalling the Duke of Newcastle who, having attended the Queen, had hurried to put himself where he thought to be before a Marquis who, in his turn being of lesser rank, had to be shown back into his place in front of the Duke. 'And why,' he grumbled to a fellow Marquis, 'should we be shoved before the Dukes? They should come before us.'

'And why,' piped his fellow peer, a near octogenerian

whose mouthful of false teeth had an uncomfortable habit of slipping, 'why s'ould I have – damn –' his top denture descended; he pushed it back, saying with a lisp since the adjustment did not exactly fit: 'Why s'ould I have to shit on thish trial? I knew her 'fore she married Kingston. Shame. Coursh they were married.'

'Twice,' from the young Earl in front who veered his head round to tell them: 'She'll get away with it I'll wager my shirt.' Which clung to his body under the heavy red robes. The April day was warm; summer had come in advance to presage winter in May. The windows high up in the walls struck shafts of light from the sun's rays on jewelled orders and the gold and gem-encrusted coronets.

The royal gallery was packed as were the seats reserved for peeresses, where sat the wives of the Dukes of Newcastle, Ancaster, and Barons, all of whom has supported and had been in the past as well as in the present, fervent admirers of 'that woman'.

The Duchess of Newcastle and her sister peeresses much resented their husbands' support of her whom they regarded as a 'husband snatcher' – or worse.

If Elizabeth Chudleigh had ever desired to be an object of interest to a whole nation, her ambition was achieved but not perhaps as she would have wished it. None the less she could not but feel, besides a natural thrill of excitement mingled with apprehension, a gratified sense of her own importance that had brought all the *beau monde*, from the Queen in her seat of honour down to the gaping herd of nobodies who had fought their way since early dawn to stand at the entrance, that they might get a glimpse of her when brought to the Hall in custody.

Mary Coke found a place behind the peeresses and between Mrs Delaney and Mrs Hannah More. Already busy taking notes, she had no thought of having had a meal before she left, but had provided herself with a hamper containing mutton chops and a lamb pie to be shared with Lady Mary and Mrs Delaney. It was also noted that the Duchesses of Newcastle and Devonshire had brought with them 'bags of good things' (according to Mrs Hannah More) 'which their rank did not exempt them from the villainous appetites of eating and drinking'. By which it might be presumed that if Mrs Hannah More regarded eating and drinking as 'villainous appetites', she must have lived as a hermit on lentils, dried peas and bread and water.

At long last, when anticipation began to be followed by boredom, the Serjeant-at-Arms stentoriously commanded 'Silence' to still the buzz of voices, chiefly feminine, chorused in a perpetual hissing of whispers as if from a colony of snakes.

'Silence!' bellowed the Serjeant-at-Arms 'on pain of imprisonment!'

'Imprisonment!' came the shocked voice of Mary Coke in the ensuing temporary lull of hissing conversation. 'How can we be imprisoned for speaking? There's no penalty surely for passing a remark?'

Then more preliminaries of interminable length, during which time all the peers were desired to 'stand up uncovered' while the Commission was read. ('Does that mean,' irrepressibly whispered Mary Coke, 'that they must disrobe and stand in their shirts?')

The reading of the Commission took close upon an hour, while the ladies refreshed themselves from the contents of the 'bags of good things' they had brought with them.

And at last all heads were craned when the Serjeant-at-Arms made proclamation for the Gentleman Usher of Black Rod to bring his prisoner to the bar.

'Oyez, oyez, oyez!' thundered through the crowded Hall. 'Elizabeth Duchess-Dowager of Kingston come forth!'

She was brought forth by the Gentleman Usher of the Black Rod, clothed head to foot in black. ('Why in

237

mourning as a widow,' commented Mrs Delaney, 'when she appeared in every colour of the rainbow while she was in Italy less than a year ago?')

'Silence!' again came the command; but there was no necessity for silence as 'the prisoner', a black hood hiding her hair, her figure completely concealed in its enveloping black silk cloak, advanced and, with supreme unruffled dignity, curtsied to her judges. When she made to curtsy low to the ground before the Lord High Steward, she was bidden, 'Madam, you may rise,' before she was down, which occasioned titters from the ladies, and grins behind their hands from the peers.

She was then conducted to the bar and still with remarkable composure took her stand. She had been attended on her entrance by two ladies, described by a reporter of the *London Chronicle* (one of the many representatives of the Press scribbling away in the seats reserved for them in the bowl of the Hall) as 'her ladies of the bedchamber', actually her maids who had attended to her dress and toilet. 'Also with her were her chaplain and her doctor.' Possibly the chaplain to give her prayerful counsel in the event of the ultimate penalty, and her doctor to render medical attention should she succumb to the ordeal.

The Lord High Steward then addressed her in a formidable speech on one tone that looked to condemn her even before she was tried.

'Madam, you stand indicted for having married a second husband, your first husband being living. A crime so destructive and so injurious in its consequences to the welfare and good order of society that by the statute law of this Kingdom it was for many years, in your sex, punishable with death.'

(More whispers from Mary Coke: 'Lucky for her if she's not hanged!')

'The lenity, however, of later times,' proceeded the Lord High Steward, 'has substituted a milder punishment

238

in its stead. This consideration must necessarily tend to lessen the perturbation of your spirits upon this awful occasion.'

If the prisoner had evinced any perturbation of spirits upon 'this awful occasion', the alternative of death to being burnt in the hand with a red hot poker might have been preferred, but throughout this monotonous indictment she had shown no fear, no 'perturbation', and seemed to be as much an interested spectator of 'this awful occasion' as if she were watching a performance by Mr Foote on the stage of the Haymarket Playhouse. He too had got himself a seat high up in the gallery, yet near enough to make a spiteful and entirely erroneous description of her appearance. 'The Duchess has small remains of that beauty of which Kings and Princes were once so enamoured. She is large and ill-shaped.' (But her 'shape' could not have been seen in the enveloping black cloak that covered her completely.) 'There was nothing,' continues Mr Foote, 'white except her face and had it not been for that she would have looked like a ball of bombazine.' (A material much used for mourning.)

Foote gave also his opinion as to 'a great deal of ceremony, a great deal of splendour and a great deal of nonsense'.

Walpole, of course, had a prominent seat and for once, after a few typical sneers, had actually some praise for her. 'The doubly noble prisoner went through her part with unusual admiration and instead of her usual ostentatious folly, her conduct was decent, even seemed natural.'

The Lord High Steward in another lengthy and repetitive speech allowed her petition to the Lords that she assume the title of the Duchess-Dowager of Kingston, and in her petition she likewise averred that Augustus John Hervey whose wife the indictment charged her with being was, at this time, the Earl of Bristol, and that accordingly she could be allowed the privilege of trial by her peers. He finally ended with the doubtful assurance that: 'From them you will meet with nothing but justice tempered with humanity.'

At this pronouncement the faintest ironical smile came upon the prisoner's white face.

Confronting the ranks of the Lords in all their glitter of coronets, jewelled orders, their crimson and ermine she, a blot of black in that dazzling assembly, spoke in a voice that rang through the Hall clearly and with no hesitation:

'My Lords, I, the unfortunate widow of your late brother, the most noble Evelyn Pierrepoint, Duke of Kingston, am brought to the bar of this Right Honourable House without a shadow of fear but infinitely awed by the respect due to you, my most honourable judges.'

In the Royal seats came a mutter from the Prince of Wales 'Hear, Hear! Why aren't I one of the judges? I'm a Duke as well as a Prince.'

'Me too,' ungrammatically from the Bishop of Osnaburgh, Duke of York. 'Why aren't we sitting in the –'

From his mother, the Queen, came admonishing frowns and a murmured 'Hush, Hush!'

The nine-year-old Princess Royal, whose cheek bulged with a sugared almond she had surreptitiously purloined from her nursery cupboard, echoed an obedient 'Hush!' and, unseen, rummaged in her pocket for another sweetmeat to replace its fast-diminishing fellow.

Said the Bishop of Osnaburgh: 'I'm hungry. I've a hole in my stomach. Is there anything to eat?'

Lady Charlotte Finch, governess to the Royal boys and this first girl born to the King, their father, had brought a hamper from Kew, where the children had their schoolrooms and nurseries, they and she having risen at dawn with the scantiest of hurried breakfasts.

'Your Royal Highness must control your hunger,' he was told by Lady Charlotte who also suffered from a hole in her stomach. 'You will have plenty to eat in the adjournment.'

240

Which at the rate the preliminaries were going looked to be in the middle of the night.

And now from the Lord High Steward came a chilly warning due to the 'respect' from the prisoner to her 'most honourable judges':

'Madam, your Ladyship will do well to give attention while you are arraigned on your indictment.'

Which went on at more repetitive length and with additions that Elizabeth Duchess-Dowager of Kingston indicted in the name of Elizabeth, wife of Augustus John Hervey, feloniously did marry and take to husband Evelyn Pierrepoint, Duke of Kingston, the said Augustus John Hervey being then alive.... 'How say you? Are you guilty of the felony whereof you stand indicted or not guilty?'

To which the prisoner replied in the same clear unhesitant voice:

'I, Elizabeth Pierrepoint, Duchess-Dowager of Kingston, indicted by the name of Elizabeth the wife of Augustus John Hervey, say I am *not* guilty.'

Clerk of the Court: 'How will you be tried?'

'By God,' was the answer, 'and my peers.'

Serjeant-at-Arms: 'Oyez, Oyez, Oyez! All manner of persons that will give evidence on behalf of our Sovereign Lord the King against Elizabeth Duchess-Dowager of Kingston, the prisoner at the bar, let them come forth ...' But before the 'manner of persons' to give evidence for the Crown came forth the prisoner was allowed to speak on her own behalf against the charge.

Standing upright at the bar she addressed the House. The Lord High Steward who was apparently deaf had desired his Lordships' leave 'to go down to the table for the convenience of hearing'.

He then removed himself to the table in front of the bar.

There with a hand to his ear he heard the Duchess of

241

Kingston deliver a speech that required of the reporters at their long trestle board much hieroglyphic scribbling.

'My Lords, my supposed marriage in the indictment with Mr Hervey, which is the ground of the charge against me, was insisted upon by him in a suit instituted in the Consistory Court of the Right Reverend Lord Bishop of London by the sentence of which Court, still in force, it was declared that I was free from all matrimonial contracts or espousals with the said Mr Hervey; and, my Lords, I am advised that this sentence, which I now desire leave to offer to your Lordships, is conclusive and that no other evidence ought to be received or stated to your Lordships respecting such pretended marriage.'

She had learned by heart this speech dictated to her by Lord Mansfield and delivered it with undismayed assurance.

The women who had come to see her judged and convicted and whose high powdered 'heads' were ornamented with all kinds of feathers, clusters of flowers as if in a miniature market garden; and a few of those whose husbands, in or out of the Lords, were naval officers or representatives of the Admiralty had decorated their headgear with a ship in full sail. All these 'heads' converged together excitedly to whisper that: 'The Chudleigh has the audacity of the devil to stand up there and defy the charge, and her husband, Bristol, not here present to contradict it.'

'She'll get off,' muttered one of the younger peers, he whose shirt had been wagered on her acquittal.

The Lord High Steward, having heard but half of the Duchess's speech, inquired of their Lordships and Counsel for the prosecution if there would be any objection to the reading of the sentence. To which the Attorney-General replied that as the prisoner was about to make some application to their Lordships he would not prevent anything she might think material to her case to lay before them.

He then went on to propound, which to the majority
of their Lordships was quite incomprehensible: Firstly,
whether the force of the sentence amounted to more than
a proof of the fraud complained of: secondly, whether a
serious sentence of such sort ought not to be admitted to
criminal prosecution. Thirdly, if such sentence created
conclusive evidence against the Crown or not ... And so
on and on for at least an hour belabouring these points
as to whether their Lordships should not dismiss the
prisoner without trial since he, the Attorney-General,
admitted he did not know how to make a more particular
answer to their Lordships' question.

Their Lordships not having asked any particular question nor received any particular answer, the prisoner then
inquired:

'If it will please your Lordships to permit my Counsel
to be heard on this point?'

The Lords (much relieved not to have to answer any
questions not yet put to them) replied with one voice:

'Ay, ay!'

Whereupon Wallace, one of the prisoner's Counsel,
spoke for an hour and a half, to end with a reading of:

'An authenticated copy of the sentence of the
Ecclesiastical Court in the year 1758 previous to the
marriage of the noble lady, the prisoner, to Evelyn Pierrepoint, Duke of Kingston, deceased.' He contended that the
prisoner who stood at their Lordships' bar was to all
intent and purpose whatsoever a single woman when she
married her deceased husband, Evelyn Pierrepoint, Duke
of Kingston. For these reasons he humbly submitted to
their Lordships that the sentence of the Ecclesiastical
Court be now conclusive evidence of the premises, that all
indictment for the felony of which the prisoner stood
charged be withdrawn.

This was received with general consternation by the
majority of their Lordships who, after all the preparations

for the trial, didn't want to see it collapse at the very onset of what to most of them was an entertainment.

The women who had sat up half the night having their 'heads' and gowns decorated for the grand occasion were equally annoyed at being deprived of that which they had looked forward to for weeks.

'Too bad,' whispered Mary Coke, 'to be done out of all the fun o' the fair!'

There then ensued more discussions and arguments between the Lord High Steward and Counsels for prosecution and defence until an adjournment was moved by the Lords, to their and everyone's relief, since they had been hard at it for eight hours without a bite to eat.

According to Walpole, who obviously thought it best to be on the side of the winning parties that looked to be a triumph for the Defence: 'The Counsels of the *twice* noble prisoner,' as he sarcastically described her, 'carried her triumphantly through the first day.'

Tired but undefeated Elizabeth, still in the custody of Sir Francis Molyneux, returned to Kingston House. She, as everybody else, had eaten nothing all day, and now at seven o'clock a dinner was sumptuously served to her and her custodian, or rather her guest, as she insisted he was.

'You don't really regard me as your prisoner, do you?' she asked him with that endearing grin of hers, more like that of a schoolboy of fifteen than a woman of fifty.

'Only, if you were,' he replied gallantly, 'I would never let you out of my sight, which is a joy to my sore eyes.'

'Sore they must be,' she said laughingly, 'having to stare at all that terrible red and crimson and gold and that fat-faced Lord High – what's his name – who is so deaf he had to sit right under my nose. Why don't he use an ear trumpet?'

While they were drinking Imperial Tokay in the drawing-room she showed Sir Francis a bullet-hole in the ceiling. 'I did that,' she told him. 'I used to practise with pistols. They stood me in good stead when my villain of

244

a banker in Rome tried to do me out of certain monies and jewels I deposited with him to prevent my return to England. Medows had, of course, put him up to it so that I should be outlawed.' And she gave him, with chuckles, the gist of her encounter with Jenkins and how she had obtained her possessions by threatening him with her money or his life! 'How,' she concluded, 'do you think this case will go? For or against me?'

'To judge by the manner in which you presented yourself today and your ability,' he twinkled, 'to deal with a villainous banker in Rome, when you make your final speech for your defence a verdict in your favour is certain.'

If he were not so certain as he professed to be, he gave her a good night's rest, which he saw she greatly needed.

She slept as soon as her head was on the pillows and, awakened with hot chocolate by her woman, was dressed and in readiness to face the second day.

This was tedious in the extreme; both the Attorney-General and the Solicitor-General refuting the argument for the defence. The Solicitor-General made a particular point relative to a forging of the Duke of Kingston's Will, suggesting that the prisoner could well have 'interfered', as he put it, with the Will. Other cases were brought forward in which a man arraigned for forgery had obtained the Will of a woman then living. . . . And so on and on *ad lib* citing case after case relating to the forging of a Will, which must have delighted Medows sitting in the gallery with his lawyer but was unintelligible and boring to the Lords, who found these whole long and tiresome citations entirely irrelevant to the case they were called upon to judge.

The Solicitor-General Dunning appeared to be suffering from a severe cold in the head accompanied by coughing, sneezing and frequent applications of two or three hand-kerchiefs in succession as they dampened. And when at last Dunning sat down it was discovered that some of his 'noble Lords' had sneaked out, probably to get something to eat and certainly to drink. Whereupon Lord Townsend, another former admirer of 'the prisoner', having seen her almost fainting with fatigue urged an adjournment.

'At once her Grace's physician was summoned,' scribbled the reporters, 'and pronounced her unfit to continue her trial for at least the next two days.'

The adjournment was then extended for three days to enable fresh tickets to be obtained when the trial was resumed. Elizabeth, whom Walpole and Co., not unjustifiably, had accused of 'shamming a faint' to give her more time to prepare her defence, returned to the fray, refreshed and determined as ever to fight and win a decisive victory.

ELEVEN

As before when brought to the bar Elizabeth maintained her outward unruffled composure while Attorney-General Thurlow proceeded with the charge against her. The story of the secret marriage at Lainston was gone into with every detail of the Duchess's life up to the time of the jactitation suit, at first dispassionately recounted. But presently Thurlow let forth violently to denounce the second marriage to the Duke of Kingston as 'the offence of bigamy, a crime punishable by death or burning of the hand'. That the Duchess had as much love and affection for the Duke as she had reason to hate Hervey was ignored.... 'Her crime in committing bigamy,' vociferated the Attorney-General, 'was moved solely by gain to enrich herself.'

His argument in respect of the jactitation suit condemned it as 'a gross and palpable evastion on the part of the Duchess'. Of Hervey's part in it he, who was equally to blame, was not mentioned. 'The prisoner, Elizabeth Hervey' (no longer the Duchess-Dowager it was noticed), 'she, and she *alone* as he would prove, must stand guilty of a heinous fraud!'

On and on he went condemning and driving home each point as so many nails in the coffin of her 'crime'. He drew their Lordships' attention to the adulterous marriage in which – 'the Duke of Kingston had been inveigled to give his unsuspecting hand to a woman who for five and twenty years had been the wife of another man!'

After taking an unconscionable time in presenting the case for the Prosecution, whereby it would seem that the prisoner was condemned before she was even tried, the first witness, Anne Craddock, was called by Solicitor-General Dunning concerning Anne's attendance on 'the prisoner' when the then Mrs Hervey went to Chelsea for the birth of her son, Henry Augustus, son of the Hon. Augustus Hervey.

Anne's evidence on oath in answer to the Solicitor-General who asked if she were in the church at Lainston with Mr Hervey and the lady and at what time of the day in the summer of 1744.

Anne Craddock: 'I was in Lainston Church with Mr Hervey and *that* lady' (pointing at '*that* lady').

The Solicitor-General: 'At what time of the day?'

Anne Craddock: 'It was at midnight not the day.'

The Solicitor-General: 'Upon what occasion?'

Anne Craddock: 'To see the marriage.'

None, all being engrossed in hearing this important witness's evidence, saw the lips of 'that lady' silently mouth the words: 'You lying bitch! You were never in the church during the ceremony.'

The Solicitor-General: 'Name the persons who were present.'

Anne Craddock: 'Mr Merrill, Mrs Hanmer, Mr Mountenay, Miss Chudleigh and myself.'

At this the prisoner was seen to make a movement forward from where she stood, one hand clenched upon the bar, the other raised when, opening her lips as if she would have spoken a denial of this evidence, a warning look from her Counsel, Mr Wallace, stayed her.

The Solicitor-General: 'Who was the clergyman?'

Anne Craddock: 'Mr Amis.'

'You saw them married?'

'Yes, I saw them married.'

The Solicitor-General: 'Did you attend the lady as her maid?'

Witness: 'I did.'

'After the ceremony did you see them in bed together?'

One of the Lords, a hand to his ear: 'Repeat what you said.'

Witness: 'I saw them put to bed and I saw them afterwards in bed that same night.'

Again the lady's lips framed the words unheard: 'You damnable liar! You never saw us in bed together at night, only in the morning.'

Asked if the lady had changed her name on her marriage, the Solicitor-General was told: 'Never. She was always known as Elizabeth Chudleigh.'

'Now, Mrs Craddock,' the voice of the Solicitor-General boomed through the Hall: 'Did you know if there were any children of this marriage?'

'I believe there was one.'

'What reason have you for so believing?'

'The lady herself told me so.'

'When you visited her in London?'

'Yes, and when I was with her at Chelsea while she was pregnant.' (Sensation in the ladies' gallery.)

And now another question bland, but equally loud, that none of the peers could miss it, even the deaf old octogenarian:

'Did the prisoner at the bar say anything particular to you about the child?'

'She told me the child was a boy and like Mr Hervey.'

It must have been apparent to a number of peers that Anne's evidence was motivated by the family of Medows and that the prosecution was bent on punishing a bigamous offence at its worst by death, at its best by burning of the hand.

Anne must have been well primed or had an aptitude for mendacity when it suited her pocket. She showed undismayed adroitness in her answers while Wallace, prisoner's Counsel cross-examining, pressed his point, steel-edged.

'Have you declared to anybody that you had expectation or some provision from the case in hand?'

'Never!' Witness, grey-haired, her face showing signs of age in its wrinkles, replied in unquavering denial: 'I could not declare it for I have had no offer made me by anyone.'

'Have you declared it? You are on oath, remember,' persisted Wallace, obviously attempting to get out of her that she had been paid to give evidence against the defence.

'Haven't I just said I could not and have *not* declared it?'

'You will answer my questions, yes or no. And whether you have declared true or false, I do not care.' Wallace laboured on trying to shake her. He couldn't. But several of the peers tackled her, particularly Lord Hillsborough who seemed to have more knowledge of how to cross-examine under the law which he and his peers represented than did Wallace himself.

An imposing figure in his crimson robes, Hillsborough, who, unlike Ancaster, had never been a suitor of 'the Chudleigh' but only wished to see justice done and the case against her indubitably proven one way or the other, asked:

'Did you ever receive any letter offering you an advantage should you appear in evidence against the prisoner?'

'Yes.' A stir like the rustle of leaves swept through the galleries where the women were seated, a stir of whispers in which Mary Coke hissed to her neighbour: 'I'll be bound she's been bribed by the Chudleigh as witness for her, and now has turned evidence against her with a higher price from Medows in her purse!'

Lord Hillsborough was belabouring Anne, if not with a birch, with his tongue.

'You say you did receive a letter offering you advantage in this case. From whom did you receive this letter?'

'From a friend of mine.'

'What have you done with the letter?'

'I don't know. I've lost it.'

'You have – *lost* it?' Up to the vaulted ceiling went Hillsborough's eyes under his grizzled brows. 'Do you maintain there was not in that letter an expression intimating that if you would appear against the prisoner at the bar a sinecure would be offered you?'

'I don't know what you mean by siney – what you said – but if you think I have accepted any – money by appearing here – well then – I haven't.'

Walpole with his customary spite had much to record of that day's doings.

'When was produced the capital witness, the ancient damsel who was present at her first marriage and tucked her up in bed, the Duchess had a temporary swoon and at intervals had to be blooded enough to have supplied her execution' . . . This as unlikely and untrue as his assertion that:

'Two babes were likewise to have blessed her nuptials, one of which for aught that appears, may exist and become the Earl of Bristol?'

What possible grounds could Walpole have had for saddling Elizabeth with 'two babes'? Unless he was reminded of her jesting remark years ago to Lord Chesterfield: 'The world says I have had twins.' And Chesterfield's amused rejoinder that he 'only believed half the world says!'

But Anne's, 'that ancient damsel's' answer to Thurlow examining her as to a message she was supposed to have received from Captain Hervey which she delivered to the Duchess: 'I told her,' said Anne, 'that Mr Hervey wanted to be divorced and the lady said she wouldn't make herself a whore *again* to oblige him!'

This caused screams of laughter from the ladies and guffaws from several Lords, suppressed by the Lord High Steward with frowns, and a bellow of 'Silence!' from the Serjeant-at-Arms.

After Hillsborough had given Anne a thorough gruelling, who did not come out of it as well as she had gone in to dodge Wallace's attack, Lord Derby, having fasted since early morning, asked for an adjournment. To this his peers readily agreed, many of them being in similar case of starvation, as also was Elizabeth, thankful for that much respite from her ordeal.

After a rest at Kingston House in the care of Black Rod, who saw to it she was sent to bed and given a hearty meal, in the morning she felt quite ready to face another day of what she called 'this ridiculous farce'. Buoyed up by Lord Mansfield and Black Rod, both now confident of her acquittal, she came composedly into the crowded Hall, prepared to hear the next witness's evidence against her.

The next witness was Anne Craddock recalled, and tackled by Lord Derby. She proved this time to be less confident under Derby's questions. Her answers were evasive but he succeeded in dragging from her that the prisoner had offered her twenty pounds a year to quit the country.

This we know was untrue because it was Anne who had suggested she should serve the Duchess for twenty pounds a year instead of accepting the thirty offered her by Medows, and had been sent back to London with only her coach fare paid.

'I have never,' she asseverated when pressed by Derby to say if she had received the twenty pounds a year offered her from the Duchess, '*never* been paid a penny piece of the annuity which she –' pointing to Elizabeth standing upright at the bar enveloped in black, only her white face expressing contempt for these atrocious lies – '*she* promised me.'

'Your assertion,' his Lordship assured her, 'can be proved. You may step down.'

Anne, somewhat the worse for wear, stepped down and was replaced by the next witness, Dr Caesar Hawkins.

The prisoner's hands were seen to cross her chest as the surgeon took the stand, either in apprehension as to what

252

he would be called upon to say, or if, so long an intimate friend, he would parry incriminating questions. Examined by Dunning, the Solicitor-General, Hawkins was put through the mill, but his answers were given with professional and unhesitating accuracy.

Elizabeth's heart went out to the good old man, her friend for so many years, now in his late sixties who she knew would fight to his last breath in her defence but never swerve from the true facts of her case, if even to her disadvantage.

Dunning: 'Did you know from either party, the prisoner and the present Lord Bristol, then Mr Hervey, that there was a marriage between them?'

Hawkins: 'From their conversation when I met them both, I believed there was a marriage but I had no proof of this, other than in conversation.'

When asked if he had known that a child was the fruit of that marriage:

'I was so told.'

'Can you tell their Lordships where this child was born?'

'At Chelsea.'

'Was this marriage and the birth of the child kept a secret?'

'I was told it had to be a secret.'

'Did you ever attend the child in the course of your profession?'

'Yes, once!'

'Were you or were you not approached by either of the parties before the commencement of this suit?'

'I was approached by the Earl of Bristol.'

'Will you tell what was the purport of Lord Bristol's approach to you?'

Up bounced Wallace, Counsel for the defence.

'My Lords. I protest on the part of the noble lady that this is hearsay and nothing said in the absence of the lady at the bar is evidence.'

Dunning (suavely): 'Very well. I will put the question in another way.' (To witness) 'Did you or did you not as result of Lord Bristol's approach to you, apply to the lady at the bar?'

'I did.'

'Then tell us the purport of Lord Bristol's application to you and what message you carried from Lord Bristol to the lady at the bar.'

There followed from Hawkins a long and detailed account of how Hervey had accosted him in the street and how he had wished to sever his matrimonial connections with the Duchess, Miss Chudleigh as she was then known, and that he wished for his freedom and had obtained it by the verdict of the Ecclesiastical Court in the jactitation suit.

This examination went on for about an hour and a half while the peers yawned and the near-octogenarian slumbered, and the ladies were bored by endless repetition concerning the birth of the child, until the Duke of Ancaster, who pointedly alluded to the prisoner as her Grace the Duchess of Kingston, was on his feet.

'Sir' (to Hawkins). 'Do you know of your *own* knowledge that the child you attended was the child of Mr Hervey and her Grace the Duchess of Kingston, or Miss Chudleigh as she was then known?'

'No, I could have no proof of that.'

Sensation among the women. The reporters looked up from their notes scenting a scandal or some unexpected revelation.

Lady Mary Coke leaned her high feathered 'head' towards Mrs Hannah More busily scribbling:

'Was she trying to pass it off as Hervey's child when it was some other man's bastard?'

'Listen.' Mrs More stayed her pencil. 'Here's Camden up.'

'She's got them all by their horns!' giggled Lady Mary into the shocked ear of Hannah More.

By Lord Camden: 'Did you ever see the child?'

'At the time of the delivery I dare say I did. Afterwards I never did.'

'Had you then any *certain* knowledge of its being the prisoner's child?'

'It is impossible for me to say when I saw it some months afterwards that I knew it to be the same child.'

By Lord Ravenscroft (the peers were now, every man of them agog for this latest evidence): 'Did you not understand that the Duchess was convinced that the sentence of the Ecclesiastical Court was final?'

'Undoubtedly so.'

'And that she was at liberty to marry again?'

'Most certainly.'

'So,' said Elizabeth when once more in the care of Black Rod she was back at Kingston House, 'it looks as if I'm acquitted. If they can't prove the child was mine and they only have my word for it, then that,' she determinedly added, 'puts an end to my marriage with Hervey if I didn't bear him his child.'

Sir Francis refilled her glass; they were at supper at the end of that long wearisome day. Trays had been brought to the drawing-room with mutton pies and pasties, fruit and wine.

'But you did bear his or – a child?'

'Not necessarily his. I have already been described by that lying bitch, Anne Craddock, as a whore. At least that is what I am supposed to have called myself.'

'Not exactly, my dear. You are supposed to have said you would not be made a whore *again*.'

'It's the same thing. So much I am supposed to have said! How can it all be proved? And how much longer will they take over this?'

Not much longer. On the following day Mrs Phillips was called and examined by the Solicitor-General.

A very different witness was Mrs Judith Phillips from the shifty and perjurious 'ancient damsel', Anne.

The Solicitor-General had her well in hand to extract from her, with infinite patience, the whole story of Mrs Hervey's visit to Winchester at the time the witness's late husband, Mr Amis, was ill in bed. How that Mr Amis had been called upon to sign an entry in a 'check book'.

'A check book?' This from the Lord High Steward still enthroned near to the bar on a chair, but now with a trumpet to his ear.

'A check book, your Grace,' suavely replied Dunning, 'as there was no register book in the church.'

'Why not?'

'So very small a parish, your Grace.'

'I see.' Which he did not; nor did he hear how an attorney had been brought in to decide if the signing of an entry of the marriage in the 'check book' could be regular, and finally given that it was.

The book was then shown to Mrs Phillips.

The Solictor-General: 'Is this the book you have been speaking of?'

Mrs Phillips looking more than ever like a trapped hare, her eyes bolting: 'Yes – I think – so long ago –'

'Look at the entry.'

The book was then handed up by the Clerk of the Court to Mrs Phillips at the open page.

'Was this entry made in your presence?'

'Yes – I think – I can't quite remember. I was in and out of the room getting my husband's supper.'

'Speak louder, please,' commanded the Lord High Steward.

This almost finished Mrs Phillips who opened her mouth but no sound came from it more than a terrified gasp.

The Solicitor-General, soothingly: 'There is no need for alarm, madam. Try and remember if this entry was made in the presence of the prisoner at the bar.'

'I believe – yes – she was in the room some of the time.'

There was a stir among the Lords and excited whispers

256

from the ladies when the Clerk of the Court read in a penetrating voice:

'Married the Honourable Augustus Hervey Esq in the parish church at Lainston to Elizabeth Chudleigh spinster, daughter of Colonel Thomas Chudleigh by me, Thomas Amis.'

Solicitor-General Dunning, with a self-satisfied smile and a bow to the Lords and the Lord High Steward: 'My Lords, I have done with this witness.'

'He has certainly done for *her*!' whispered the irrepressible Mary Coke.

'For whom?' Mrs Hannah More poised her pencil to ask.

'Why, the Chudleigh, of course.'

'*Cela dépend*. Here is Mansfield, another of her Counsel, cross-examining.'

Mr Mansfield, a nephew of Lord Mansfield, was putting the now petrified Mrs Phillips through a kind of third degree. He extracted from her that both she and her husband – her present husband – had at one time been in the service of the Duke of Kingston and later had all their expenses paid by Mr Medows.

'For what purpose?'

'When he left – when he – when my husband left.'

'He was turned out?'

'No – that is –'

'I put it to you that your husband, Mr Phillips, was given his notice to leave the service of the Duke of Kingston?'

'I think – he was – was not.'

After considerable brow-beating of the unhappy Mrs Phillips her inquisitor succeeded in making her admit that she saw the entry of the marriage in the register.

'Signed by your husband?'

'No, not my husband – not Mr Phillips – Mr Amis, the clergyman.'

'We quite understand which of your husbands

married Miss Chudleigh to Mr Hervey, a marriage that had been proven null and void.'

The Lord High Steward, the trumpet to his ear :

'I object to that remark. Their Lordships have not yet found either marriage null and void.'

'Certainly, your Grace, I withdraw the remark. Now, Mrs Phillips, I will not detain you much longer. If, as you say, you were back and forth from the room at the time of this entry in the register – or as it is called the "check book" – how came you to see the register of the marriage ?'

'My husband, Mr Amis, he read it to me and –' the poor woman was now in a pitiable state – 'he was ill in bed.'

'So you have said. You have also said that Mr Medows defrayed your expenses after you and your husband left the Duke of Kingston's service. How often have you seen Mr Medows ?'

'Once or – or twice.'

'I suggest more frequently than that and that you have recently met Mr Medows and talked with him of any benefit you might gain from the evidence you would give against this case.'

Mrs Phillips on the verge of collapse : 'I didn't – I don't want to – I –'

'Thank you, Mrs Phillips.'

Mr Mansfield's countenance, cherubic, rosy-cheeked, expanded in a smile of considerably more satisfaction than that of the lady's examiner the Solicitor-General, who looked anything but satisfied and was biting his lip as if he would bite it off.

'Thank you. . . .' faintly uttered Mrs Phillips as she tottered from the box.

The next important witness was the Rev. James Trebeck, who produced the register of St Margaret's Westminster and read from it the entry of :

Marriage in 1769. The most Honourable Evelyn

Pierrepoint, Duke of Kingston, Bachelor, and Elizabeth Chudleigh of Knightsbridge were married by special licence of the Archbishop of Canterbury this eighth day of March 1769, by me Samuel Harpur between us

> Kingston
> Elizabeth Chudleigh
> in the presence of:

Then came the names of several witnesses of the marriage including a Dr Collier, one of the advocates to Elizabeth Hervey at the time the Ecclesiastical Court had pronounced their decision declaring the marriage of Elizabeth Chudleigh to the Hon. Augustus Hervey null and void.

This ended the case for the prosecution, when their Lordships were thankful to be told by the Lord High Steward that there was to be an adjournment until the following Monday.

Now came the fifth and final day of the trial when the Duchess must address the House and present her evidence. In those days the onus of defence rested solely on the prisoner as Counsel could only examine witnesses and not the accused.

Elizabeth had lain awake almost the whole night before rehearsing and reading her speech, most of which, save for Lord Mansfield's guidance and suggestions, she had written herself. And with the same dauntless courage that had sustained her throughout her tremendous ordeal she faced the House of Lords, reading from her notes, with extempore additions and in a clear firm voice, the whole lengthy oration which might well have done justice to that brilliant up and coming young parliamentarian Charles James Fox: he who a few years later was to have so great an influence on the Prince of Wales, his 'dear Charles'.

Even Walpole grudgingly allowed that she 'pronounced well'.

To give her speech in its entirety would fill pages. Only

the bare essentials are here recorded. Her chief difficulty and stumbling block to her defence was the testimony of Anne Craddock. Of Augustus Hervey she said very little, but the decision of the Ecclesiastical Court having been set aside, her case was rendered the more difficult to prove. None the less she could vehemently protest her innocence of the charge against her, and with such eloquence and reference to the authorities who had sanctioned her marriage, that it looked as if, despite all opposition, she might yet be acquitted.

Dressed as before in deep black that enveloped her from head to foot, her face so white under those sombre trappings none who saw her could but admire her fortitude, even those who most decried her.

'My Lords, I have suffered unheard of persecutions. My honour has been severely attacked. I have been loaded with reproaches and such indignities and hardships to make me less able to present my defence before this august assembly and a prosecution of so extraordinary a nature and so undeserved.'

At this the rows of encrimsoned robes and coronets moved as if swayed by a breeze as the peers' heads nodded assent or shook in disapproval of her statement that her prosecution was 'so undeserved'.

'My Lords, I appeal to the feelings of your hearts whether it is not cruel that I should be brought as a criminal to a public trial for an act committed under the sanction of the law – an act honoured by His Majesty's most gracious approval, and previously known to my Royal Mistress, the late Princess Dowager of Wales, and likewise authorized by Ecclesiastical jurisdiction.'

'She's made a good point there,' murmured Mrs Hannah More busily scratching away at her notes.

'She has the gift of the gab well enough,' returned Mary Coke in a stage whisper. 'She's dressed herself for the part and plays it as if on the boards, where she should be. She has missed her vocation.'

'My Lords,' the Duchess's voice was raised a tone higher, 'had these persecutions been set on foot for the love of justice or good example for the community, why did they not institute their prosecution during the five years when I was received and acknowledged the undoubted and unmolested wife of the late Duke of Kingston? Surely your Lordships will not discredit so reputable a Court and disgrace those judges who so legally and honourably presided. . . .'

On this pronouncement Elizabeth and her Counsel had pinned their faith that it was over the judgement of the Ecclesiastical Court on which the case was fought.

Walpole, listening all ears, said to Horace Mann seated next to him:

'There is not one person in the whole burlesque in this Hall who is not as much convinced of her bigamy as of their own existence.'

Walpole was wrong. Half the Lords still remained convinced that the prisoner's marriage to the Duke of Kingston must be legal or else to defy Ecclesiastical jurisdiction.

Elizabeth, unswervingly pursuing her defence, told the judges that her marriage to the Duke of Kingston, besides the decision of the Ecclesiastical Court, had been sanctioned by a Doctor of law, Dr Collier. Before the actual marriage ceremony was performed she had consulted him to make certain that the Right Reverend Father in God, the Lord Bishop of London, did pronounce their prisoner, then Elizabeth Chudleigh now Elizabeth Duchess-Dowager of Kingston, free from all previous matrimonial contracts or espousals. . . . 'My Lords, the loss I have sustained in my most kind companion and affectionate husband, my late noble Lord, with regard to the motives that induced his Grace to disinherit his eldest nephew, I particularly requested my Counsel to abstain from any reflections upon my adversaries that the nature of their prosecution so much deserved. I am now reduced to the sad necessity of saying that the late Duke of Kingston was made acquainted with the fatal cruelty with which Mr Evelyn Medows treated an unfortunate lady who was as amiable as she was virtuous, falsely to declare that he broke his engagement with her for fear of displeasing the Duke. This, with his cruelty to his mother and sister and his attempt to quit active service in the late war, highly offended the Duke and made it difficult for him to continue friendly intercourse with Mr Medows for upward of eighteen years.'

She scored a point there. She had adroitly brought in the motive for this prosecution activated by Medows to disprove her marriage with his uncle Kingston in order to dispute the Will that she was not his widow as she had never been his wife.

'My Lords, I call upon Almighty God –' she raised her hand and her eyes on high – 'to witness that at the time of my marriage with the Duke of Kingston I had the most perfect conviction that it was lawful. That noble Duke to whom every passage of my life had been disclosed and whose affection for me and his own honour would never have suffered him to have married me had he not, as well as myself, received the solemn assurance from Dr Collier that the sentence passed by the Ecclesiastical Court was absolutely final and conclusive. It was on the legal advice of Dr Collier that I married my husband, his Grace the Duke of Kingston, and who was present at the marriage. I now request –' she paused to deliver her request in a voice that rang through the Hall – 'that Dr Collier be examined!'

Her impassioned address and the facts she disclosed, in particular the motive of the dastardly Medows, who, had he not disputed the Will there would have been no case of bigamy or of unlawful marriage, had its effect upon the peers. At this last appeal one of them – Ancaster – was on his feet, exclaiming:

'In the Name of God let us give the prisoner every

indulgence. It appears she was influenced to marry on the advice of Dr Collier, Doctor of Law. I do beg, as the Duchess desires, that Dr Collier may be examined.'

Here was a bitter stroke of fate. While all agreed that Dr Collier should be called as witness to the prisoner's avowal, the defence was held up for an hour's adjournment until Dr Collier's personal physician sent word that the doctor was ill of a severe fever and could not leave his bed; but evidence might, if their Lordships agreed, be taken at the sick man's bedside.

This suggestion was not received with general assent. Lord Camden, speaking for the Law Lords, declared that never had so unusual a course been pursued. But another of the peers cried out:

'If there has ever been any such instance let it be produced. And in God's name let justice be done!'

But in God's name justice was not to be done. The fates were all against her since so important a witness as Dr Collier could not give evidence from his bed.

The case drew wearily to its close after several more witnesses for the defence had been examined and dismissed. The Attorney-General then made a long and dreary speech heard with infinite boredom, for all the peers were impatiently waiting for the curtain to fall on the last act of the whole distasteful drama.

When at last he had finished Thurlow sat, and their Lordships filed out to the Chamber of Parliament to consider their verdict.

Elizabeth was taken by Black Rod to an inner room. There, motionless, wordless, she sat while Sir Francis Molyneux essayed to tell her with doubtful optimism:

'Whichever way it goes, I and all those who do not sit in judgement on you, believe you to be innocent of felony. And you have the privilege as a peeress of claiming your right not to suffer the burning of your hand.'

'A barbaric penalty even for a common felon.' A small wintry smile came upon her lips. 'I know and God knows

263

I am innocent. Therefore what matters if a body of my Peers judge me guilty of an offence I have never committed? I understand that in the Church of Rome there is no mortal sin committed unless with deliberate intent. Men have been hanged who are innocent of murder. Let them judge not lest they be judged.'

The debate on the decision of the Peers in the Chamber of Parliament went on for three hours, an eternity to her who waited to hear her doom.

Sir Francis ordered a warm drink and food to be brought to her. She refused it and bade him: 'Please – leave me. I wish to be alone. I'll not try to escape. You can lock the door and you and my guards can wait outside.'

Black Rod left her. She sank on her knees, not to pray but to review, as if drowning every incident of her life; forms and faces long vanished passed before her in minutest detail. They whom she had known, had loved, drew near to take her by the hand and lead her back along the paths of memory. For, she said, to those whose lives are ending or outlived there is no life but memory. . . .

A Devon lane, a girl, her ripe lips stained with the juice of blackberries, a rider coming out of a wood to find her there, he who first had brought her to the Court of her Princess, as Maid of Honour. . . . A youth who knelt before her, his head buried in her knees. 'I love you, shall love you for ever. I will write to you from every port. . . .' He too had gone. All of them gone, never a letter from him whose wife she would have been. A dark night and the glimmer of a candle in a little church. A young naval officer . . . 'O God!' the cry broke from her, 'that night of nights which has brought me to this!' And then, her one and only marriage with her own beloved husband. Gone. He too gone – where? I am the Resurrection and the Life. . . . I believe, help thou my unbelief.

From the Chamber after that interminable period while her peers considered their verdict they at last filed back into the Hall.

'Your Grace.' Black Rod had entered to find her calm and composed. 'Come. Your judges have returned.'

Her hand in his, her head upraised, her eyes tearless, and in her heart a prayer: 'Thy Will, not mine, be done,' she was led back to the bar where for five days she had stood in purgatory, now to hear herself condemned – or saved.

The Lord High Steward, enthroned on high, put to each peer in his slow montonous voice the same question:

'Is it your Lordship's opinion that the prisoner at the bar is guilty or not guilty of the felony of which she is charged?'

And each of the peers, her judges, answered, some falteringly, some determinedly, hand on heart:

'Guilty upon mine Honour.'

She closed her eyes but could not close her ears to those answers forced from each one however reluctantly. Ancaster's lips moved to the almost silent words ... 'upon mine honour'. Only the Duke of Newcastle, tears springing to trickle down his ruddy cheeks, he who had known and secretly loved her since she was a girl spoke, his hand on his heart:

'Guilty but erroneously, *not* intentionally, upon mine honour.'

She had been prepared for it. Standing upright, unmoved, as a statue might have stood, so colourless her face; yet serene and calm to the last, she drew from under her black cloak a paper which she had written the day before should her case be lost. And in it she prayed the privilege of her peerage, that she be saved of being burnt in the hand, the penalty for bigamy.

The Attorney-General whose face, granite-hard, beetle-browed, offered no mercy, subjected the peers to a harsh argument that a woman whether peeress or not must be disallowed any such privilege. He was upheld by Dunning, the Solicitor-General, that the hideous penalty must be observed.

But Ancaster and Camden demanded that the prisoner's prayer should be granted as her right to share such privilege with her peers. 'For she is, as Bristol's wife,' emphatically declared Ancaster, 'a peeress!'

The Lord High Steward then addressed her:

'Madam, the Lords have considered your prayer and do allow it to you. But, Madam, let me add that although little punishment or none can now be inflicted upon you, your own conscience will supply the defect. But, Madam, let me warn you that should you be found guilty a second time of a similar offence you will incur capital punishment.'

At this several of the peers covered their mouths to hide their grins at the unconscious humour of that pronouncement – an injunction to the prisoner not to commit bigamy a second time.

'I am further to inform you,' droned the Lord High Steward, 'that you are discharged from paying your fees and that you are no longer a prisoner.'

Great was the dismay of Hannah More, of Mary Coke, of Mrs Delaney and, not the least, of Walpole, who all discussed, wrote and enjoyed what they called 'the shame and ignominy brought upon the ex-Duchess of whom the law had declared her marriage to the Duke of Kingston to be void and she a bigamist – to go unpunished!'

So Evelyn Medows gained nothing from his attempt to disprove the Will of the Duke, his uncle, which brought him only financial loss; and Mrs Delaney had the satisfaction of telling her friends that:

'Elizabeth, calling herself Duchess of Kingston, was this very day unduchessed and narrowly escaped being burnt in the hand.'

Hannah More made no secret of *her* satisfaction at the verdict.

'The shameless Duchess is degraded into as shameless a Countess. Surely there was never so thorough an actress.

Garrick says: "She so much out-acted him it is time for him to leave the stage." '

'Their tittle-tattle is for me less than water on a duck's back,' Elizabeth told her faithful Sir Francis when he returned with her to Kingston House, where she had ordered a sumptuous dinner for those peers who had pronounced against her and were still her friends especially, '*Et tu Brute*,' she said to Ancaster, who had been invited with Lord Mansfield and others. No women, only men, were her guests.

'I had to agree with the evidence against you, yet it hurt me more than you, upon mine honour.'

'But why did you all disavow the Ecclesiastical Court's jurisdiction? That I shall never understand. Although, as Walpole has said and says again, "the Law is a liar" – as great a liar as he maintains am I!'

She did not entertain her guests later than midnight and sent them from her after they had dined and wined so plenteously that their lackeys had all to do to heave them into their coaches.

She went to bed and slept soundly for the first time in a week and woke to a bright sun-drenched day. Through a chink in the pink-lined curtains a dazzle of light pierced a golden shaft to strike at her sleep-laden eyelids and bring her to wakefulness, alert for the business of the morning.

Calling for her woman she ordered her breakfast, and when the tray was brought she bade her open the curtains. As she drank her chocolate and nibbled toasted rusks she pursued her plans already half formed and now a certainty.

She would leave London, England – her England – so fraught with memories, bitter-sweet, and seek forgetfulness in a new life and new adventures. Yes, she thought with wry humour, I am a born adventuress and I will travel where the spirit moves me to find myself again. For I have lost myself in all these awful months of waiting until the trial that has ended in what I feel to be no defeat for me but a victory. As for Medows, he is the loser. Forgive your enemies ... in this first golden day of her freedom, she could forgive and more than forgive him, compensate him for the financial loss he had sustained in disputing his uncle's Will believing that she, as his uncle's mistress and not his wife nor widow according to the judgement of her peers, had no right to the Kingston estate. But Medows was wrong. No matter that the Duke's Will had left his wife his whole estate absolutely, the word 'wife' stood for the woman Elizabeth, although proven not his wife but none the less his sole heiress.

The whole ghastly farce, or burlesque (as Walpole calls it, she reflected with a twisted smile), is a miscarriage of justice. Since the Ecclesiastical Court made me his legal and undisputed wife, how came they to disprove it?

She could, of course, appeal, but what the use? Enough of the Law. Let it abide. She knew, and God knew, she was not and never had been the wife of any man other than her own beloved husband whose widow she was and would remain so to her dying day....

'Your Grace,' her servants still addressed her by the title of which her peers had deprived her, 'a gentleman has called. He gives no name but asks to see your Grace most urgently.'

'I can see no one who will not give his name.' Then thinking it might be – why not? – Medows come to ask if she were prepared to pay his costs, she said: 'Tell him to wait. I will see him.'

No longer gowned in black, her hair unpowdered, its sprinkling of grey in the warm brown curls, lent to her still youthful face an added beauty; her eyes, as blue, unfaded as when she was a girl, her bared neck firm, unlined, she went to meet him. At the door she halted, her heart in a hurry to shape his name faltering upon her lips ... 'You! Hervey ... As always,' she gained strength to say, 'you force an entrance on me.'

268

'I ask your pardon,' he came to her. 'I am here on a mission that is to me of utmost urgency.'

'Be seated,' she gestured him to a chair, but he stood while she said, her tone cold as the cold of her fingers that played with a jewel at her breast: 'Of what urgency have you to do with me? My case is lost, yet I am still the victor in my judgement and in God's sight. I am the wife – no, alas, the widow of Kingston, and I bide by the law that made marriage to you, Hervey, void.'

'That is why I am here.' He spoke decisively but with muted passion. 'Our marriage, as your and my peers have proved, is *not* void. I am your lawful husband and I claim you as – my wife. It is not too late.' He approached, nearing her, his face whitened, his mouth in tremble. 'I have this to say. Whatever in the past I have done and which you rightly consider is unpardonable, believe me if I tell you I have never ceased to regret it and – you will not believe this but it is God's truth – nor ceased to love you. When I watched you all those awful days – no wait! Let me finish. Unseen I watched you there in the Hall. I saw with what courage you contested the prosecution of our peers and I knew what I have lost. I too have courage, but not so great as yours, to combat my country's enemies, for I did not stand alone to fight *our* battles. You did stand alone and unsupported. Elizabeth – I want you – my wife. You *are* my wife. Will you not take me? Let us live out our lives together, you and I, husband and wife, which we are and ever have been.'

She heard him out in silence, stirred by conflicting emotions. Doubt that what he asked could be for his own advantage, the Kingston heritage which was hers and if his wife, he, her husband, could lay claim to it. . . . But the sight of his quivering lips, his strained eyes, and a small muscle of tension moving in his tightened jaw dissolved that doubt of him. So he was feeling something deeply. Love? Passion? Or – no, not avarice. Not passion. Could it after all these years be love, the love of the youth who had married her on that dark fatal night and who had taken her, as he had learned from his fellows at sea deprived of their normal manhood never for months to be within sight or touch of women? Had she condemned him too hardly? . . . Yes, and she would make amends, but not as he would wish it.

'Hervey, hear me. I have long forgotten, or put away from me the hurt and shame I suffered on our marriage night. I blame not you, not now. But I can never be your wife for I am not your wife. I have never been the wife of any man except the man I married lawfully, for I abide by the decision of the Court that gave me to Kingston as his wife. And I am and will always be his widow. I leave this week, or as soon as may be, for France and then – who knows? I shall begin a new life in a new world – alone.'

She held out her hand to him. He took it in both of his.

'I think,' he said unsteadily, 'that I have never loved you, as you deserved to be loved, until now. My cause is lost – has always been lost. You belonged and do belong to Kingston – in the sight of God. And so –'

'And so –' a suspicious brightness was in her eyes of tears unshed – 'forget me. You may divorce me if you will and if you can to cite the dead and – marry again.'

'God Almighty!' He released her hand, fell back a step or two. Incredulity struggled with the knowledge that here was a woman of irresistible unconscious generosity, as of a child who gives up its toys to another. Yes, this in her, he realized, was her childlike greed for power, her love of rank – that he had always known – but only now did he understand she was guileless, unaware that she turned a knife in his heart even while he choked back an upsurge of laughter.

'You absurd, adorable –' he kissed her hands slowly, first one and then the other. 'Do you really think I would marry any woman but you who are my true and lawful wife, as our peers have judged us? But have it as you will. Not as *I* would will it. We can't pay all our debts in life. Mine will be paid to you hereafter. We part –' his voice broke – 'as friends?'

'Dear,' she said and her lips brushed his in the lightest fugitive touch, 'there are no debts on either side. I go my way and you go yours and – God be with you.'

'And also', he answered on an indrawn breath, 'with you.'

Then he bowed and went from her blindly, never to see her again.

EPILOGUE

There is so much more to tell of the further adventures of this extraordinary woman who has been so cruelly maligned by her contemporaries that it would fill another volume.

Sufficient to say that when she left England after the nine days – or rather five days – wonder of her famous trial which made history without precedent in the House of Lords, she started on her travels through Europe.

As ever she had a following of men who pursued her with avowals of unending love; some indubitably sincere and others attracted more by her enormous wealth than by her. But to her determination to remain the widow of her one and only husband, Kingston, she held herself immune from their advances. She refused men of eminence and rank. Prince Radzivil, a Polish prince, was on his knees to her with the offer of his principality, but she declined to be his wife. She remained his friend and received him with the same aloof indulgence accorded to her many suitors; never anything more.

Yet unlike the women of the English Courts she was a favourite with all the great ladies of Europe, Russia, Vienna, where the Electress of Saxony, her old-time friend, bestowed upon her the title of Countess of Warth.

During her visit to Russia she became the favourite of the great Empress Catherine who delighted in her wit and her inimitable mimicries of other crowned heads whom she had met, and told stories of her life in England, and not the least her humorous account of the famous trial.

In Elizabeth, the Empress Catherine recognized the

courage that had overcome such devastating persecution and with such wonderful recuperative resilience; a woman after her own heart.

She was received everywhere not only as Countess of Bristol but as the sole inheritor of the Duke of Kingston's vast wealth, whose lawful wife many believed her to have been, despite that judgement had gone against her.

News of her triumphant reception in the European capitals reached London and the usual gossip about her was floated into legend. Mrs Delaney who had rejoiced to see her 'unduchessed' wrote to one of her numerous correspondents:

'Mademoiselle Chudleigh-Hervey-Bristol is now or may be Princess Radzivil and Queen of Poland.' *(sic)*. . . . Walpole also had his say, more venomous than ever. 'Your Duchess of Kingston is a paltry mountebank. It is too ridiculous to give herself airs after her conviction.'

What Walpole and the rest of them did not know that she, now sixty and still possessed of that ineffable charm which had conquered men throughout her chequered career met, while on her travels, a man of singular attraction and many titles to impress and almost conquer her: Prince Annibale, Duke of St Saba, Count Worta, the latter name by which he was most known. He fell, or professed to fall, madly in love with her, offered her marriage, begged, as they all did, for her favour, but she refused to accept him either as husband or lover, even after Bristol had died. That he fascinated her is certain and that they exchanged an intimate, and on his side, passionate correspondence. . . . 'You are the wonder of your age, deserving celebrity to the end of time.'

His account of himself gave it he was an Albanian Prince, that Prince Henry of Prussia – another of Elizabeth's admirers – and also the Emperor of Germany, were his intimate friends.

All this Elizabeth took with a pinch of apocryphal salt. Nor was she much disillusioned when the true facts of his life were divulged to her in an extravagant letter of confession.

'Elizabeth,' it ran, 'I admit I am but a low adventurer born in the humblest grade of society. I have learned the manners and deportment of a prince although my father was an ass-driver in Trebizond. . . . Have I not succeeded in deceiving the wisest heads in Europe? But I look with contempt on the whole human race except you – you being the only soul I have ever loved. In these last moments of my adventurous life I cannot refrain from saying how great would have been my happiness could I bear with me into eternity the hope that my memory will not be hateful to you. . . .'

His real name was Stiepan and his assumed titles in various countries were legion. He had swindled Elizabeth out of vast sums of money on some pretext or other, and of loans that would be advantageous to her in accumulative interest. She, no business woman, was never loth to gamble. But she bore him no grudge. She blamed herself rather than him for being so easily duped.

He was arrested in Amsterdam for forgery. The day after his arrest he committed suicide in prison with poison contained in his ring.

Of course the English-speaking world, or those who had known her in her triumphant heyday, linked this swindler's name with hers as his accomplice in crime, but as all such rumours ascribed to her were false they died their natural, or unnatural, death and were forgotten.

Reckless, erratic, unpredictable, an enigma to the end of her meteoric career, she spurned the scandal-mongers who have besmirched her name for all posterity.

And yet the worst that can be said of her is that she bigamously, if innocently, married the one and only man of whom to her dying day she believed herself to be the lawful wife.

274

True to her conscience she did not forget Medows, who had sought to bring about her ruin and convict her of a hideous penalty if not imprisonment. Not only did she defray the ruinous costs of his case because she felt he had reason to dispute his uncle's Will, thinking her to be Kingston's mistress and not his wife, but she allowed him six hundred a year and bequeathed him in *her* Will fifteen thousand pounds and all her gold and silver plate.

She died on 28 August 1788 at the house she had bought on her estate at St Assise outside Paris, unmourned by all who had known her in England but loved to the last by the great European women of her time, not the least of them the Empress Catherine of Russia. She outlived her husband, or him who she denied was her husband, the Earl of Bristol, by many years.

Her end was typically courageous and not without that touch of humour which had upheld her in all her misfortunes and triumphs. She could always laugh at herself or at the Fates.

She had not been well for the last few weeks, defied her doctor's orders, entertained lavishly, stayed out at functions and banquets until all hours. At her age, sixty-eight, her gaieties and gallantries were too much for her. She broke a small blood vessel. Nothing serious, her medical advisers assured her, but insisted she must rest in bed for at least a week. She obeyed her doctor for a day or two; then was up and about, driving in the Bois de Boulogne in Paris, shopping and buying gifts for her friends, returned home, said she felt tired and bade her attendants: 'Bring me a glass of madeira.'

She drank it at a draught and asked for more. A gleam of laughter crossed her face. 'Good wine has never failed me. I could drink a hogshead and not turn a hair. But I'll rest awhile before my visitors arrive tonight.'

She lay down upon her couch. Her women watched

beside her. 'You need not wait,' she told them. 'Leave me now.'

Her eyelids sank.

They left her sleeping there. And when they came to robe her for her guests she was still asleep. . . .

Nor did she wake.

Authorities Consulted

Trial of the Duchess of Kingston edited by Lewis Melville,
    1927
An Authentic Detail of Particulars, 1788
Letters and *Journal* of Lady Mary Coke
Letters of Mrs Hannah More
Letters of Lady Mary Wortley Montagu
Letters of Horace Walpole
The Four Georges by W. M. Thackeray
The Amazing Duchess by C. E. Pearce, 1911
Royal George by C. E. Vulliamy, 1937
English Social History by G. M. Trevelyan, 1942
Life of Foote by Percy Fitzgerald, 1910
Bath by R. A. L. Smith
Dictionary of National Biography
Gentleman's Magazine, Lady's Magazine, etc.

Also available by

DORIS LESLIE

PARAGON STREET

'Abounds in period colour.'   *Daily Telegraph*

THE SCEPTRE AND THE ROSE

'Doris Leslie tells her story from the point of view of Catherine, showing her as innocent and great-hearted, the warm centre of a novel which, because it deals with a violent and tumultuous period of our history, never lacks excitement or romance.'
Good Housekeeping

THE MARRIAGE OF MARTHA TODD

'Miss Leslie is one of those women authors who have an almost psychic contact with their characters . . . brilliantly portrays the Victorian double-attitude to sex.'   *Sunday Express*

THE REBEL PRINCESS

'Doris Leslie . . . plunges the reader right into the intrigue and debaucheries of a court dedicated, it seemed, to anything rather than ruling the country.'
Books and Bookmen

A YOUNG WIVES' TALE

(A sequel to *Folly's End* and *The Peverills*)

'Miss Leslie has given to her story a certain political seasoning; there is reference to the unrest – industrial and social – that was so marked a feature of life both in Britain and elsewhere during the early years of the last century.'   *Guardian Journal*

THE DESERT QUEEN

'Colourful mixture of T. E. Lawrence and Elinor Glyn.'   *The Sunday Times*

THE DRAGON'S HEAD

'An accomplished romance.'   *Books and Bookmen*

The Uniform Edition of
Doris Leslie's works